the three treasures

myths of old japan

MIRIAM COX AUTHOR OF *The Magic and the Sword*

KINGO FUJII *Illustrations*

HARPER & ROW, Publishers

Evanston, Illinois • Elmsford, New York • Pleasanton, California, and New York, New York

author and artist

MIRIAM COX's interest in Oriental mythology was first stimulated by the little seventeen-syllable Japanese poems called "haiku," which are described later in this book. Like the haiku, many Japanese myths express the deeply rooted interest in nature that is a part of the Japanese culture and temperament. Mrs. Cox found interesting parallels between the myths of Japan and the Greek myths, with which she has been familiar since childhood and which she has used extensively in her classrooms.

She teaches world literature at Fullerton Junior College, in California, and children's literature at Orange State College.

KINGO FUJII has been deeply involved in Japanese tradition since his birth in Hawaii. His father was an artist and an instructor in the dramatics of the Kabuki dance-dramas. His mother was a musician, specializing in teaching the samisen, a three-stringed lute-like instrument.

Mr. Fujii attended the University of Hawaii, studied at the Honolulu Academy of Art and the Art Institute of Chicago, and worked under master artists in Japan.

ᴅᴇᴀʀ ʀᴇᴀᴅᴇʀ:

These are the tales of old Japan. Some are gentle, some are amusing, some tell of violent men and bitter struggles. There are fierce animals, and timid animals in need of help, and animals that help men. There are people who are brave or clever or foolish or villainous, there is a great deal of magic, and above all there are the gods, which in Japan are many and ever-present.

Every land has its myths, most of which are now just old stories to tell and re-tell. Still, the events and the names of characters can be deeply rooted in everyday language. From the Greek myths we still use "Ajax" and "Venus" and "Atlas" to name products. We still speak of Trojan horses and Homeric battles and Herculean strength without perhaps realizing that these expressions are taken directly from the old tales. Miriam Cox recounts the Greek myths, and points out how they still have life in the Twentieth Century, in her book *The Magic and the Sword*.

Some of the myths of Japan are more than just stories, too. The three treasures described here are very real, and have existed for many centuries. The sword, the mirror, and the jewels are part of Japan's royal treasures. They stand as symbols not only of Japan's long history but also of her present status as a modern nation. They are used symbolically at least in the coronation ceremonies when a Japanese emperor is crowned.

A word about the illustrations. Basically they follow the rather strict rules that have governed Japanese art for centuries. They were painted with the traditional ink and brush. However, there is in them a strong story-telling element that the old Japanese art forms did not stress as much as we do.

pronouncing

japanese words

People in all parts of the world need to say the same things. Every language must have in it some way to say "I don't feel very well today," and "Let's take a walk," and "You are a very pretty girl." Every language does not necessarily need words for Christmas, or football, or geometry, but it certainly must have words and phrases that let people talk to each other about everyday things.

For instance, it would be hard to imagine any language that didn't have names for months. Maybe in some places they have thirteen months instead of twelve, but there are names. Everywhere there will be a word for "Hello," which will be different from "Good morning." There will certainly be words for left and right, horse and dog, river and mountain.

You will find some Japanese words throughout this book, and it isn't hard to learn to pronounce them. First of all, every Japanese word ends in a vowel (a, e, i, o, or u) or in n. Now, those vowels sound different from ours. Each of our vowels in English has many different sounds; for instance, think of the many sounds we give to a, as in father, cat, hall, make. But not in Japanese. You always give a vowel one sound, and you give it that sound every time you see it.

For example, there is a Japanese word that looks like one of our English words: sake. We would want to pronounce it as we would pronounce the English word in "For goodness' sake." Instead, pronounce the a as in father, and the e as in men. Now, don't hold those vowel sounds very long. Don't drawl them. Pronounce them as quickly as you can, while still giving them the proper sound. That's the way the Japanese do it. (Incidentally, sake is a kind of drink made from rice.) And don't give that e on the end the long e sound, which an English speaker is likely to do. Don't say sock ee. That e should have the sound of e as in get.

Another thing that English speakers find a little hard is that the Japanese do not stress syllables in a word as we do. That is, we say cam' el, im por' tant, com mit'. But now say those words without syllable stress. That would be the Japanese way.

Do the vowel sounds this way:

a as in father
e as in bed
i as in machine
o as in for
u as in bush

You have to be careful about combinations of two vowels. Suppose that there were a Japanese word spelled pain. You couldn't use the long a sound for the ai. You would have to pronounce the a as in father and the i as in police.

All consonants are pronounced about like English consonants, except that the g is always "hard" and is never given the j sound. If g is at the beginning of a word, say it as you would in English in the word give. If the g is inside the word it sounds more like ng.

It will never be at the end of a word because all Japanese words end with a vowel or with n. And the n at the end of a word is never slurred over. It is given its full n sound as if it were a separate syllable.

The letter-combination ch is really like a separate letter of the alphabet and is pronounced as we would pronounce it in cherry.

When you think about breaking up a Japanese word into syllables, remember that a vowel is never separated from the consonant that precedes it. For instance you would never say kim-o-no or kim-on-o, but always ki-mo-no.

Once in a while there is a mark over a vowel thus û or maybe it is written thus ū. When that happens, just hold the vowel sound a little longer. For instance, in English we usually hold the u in lure a little longer that we hold the u in put. The Japanese city Kyûshû has two accented u's. Hold them about as long as you hold the u in lure. Sometimes you find that ky combination of letters as in Kyûshû. Say them the same way you say the beginning of the English word cute. The word Tokyo, then, is not toe kee o, but toke yo.

Once in a while there is a double vowel. In this book is a character called Susanoo. That isn't a sound like the oo in look or in moon. It is just two "o" sounds pronounced one after the other, as when we say "Oh, oh."

Want to practice a little? Tori means bird. How do you pronounce the o? The i? The syllables will be to ri, not tor i. Will either syllable be stressed? No. Therefore our pronunciation will be something like taw ree.

Sakura means cherry blossoms. Syllables: sa ku ra. No syllable stress. Keep the vowels very short. And never pronounce a u as we do in our pure. The Japanese u never sounds like yoo; but always like oo.

O-hayô gozaimasu. That's good morning. Not really as hard as it looks. Break up the first word into syllables: o ha yô (with a long vowel sound). Say it a few times. No syllable stress, therefore it won't sound quite like our state of Ohio. Second word: go zai ma su. In that second syllable both the a and the i will be sounded.

One more, and then you are on your own: Okurete môshiwake gozaimasen. It means "I'm sorry to be late."

o ku re te mo shi wa ke go zai ma sen

contents

Part **thREE**   *White Banners of the Minamoto, page 161*

eight hundred myriads

of gods

"The way of the gods." This is the meaning of the Japanese 11
word "Shinto." So short a word to mean so much, for the story
of Shinto leads us into pathways that have their origins deep in
the past, before there was heaven, earth, gods, or men. As we
follow these paths through the forests of time, we watch divine
beings coming miraculously into existence. Then we see two
creator deities who, after a quaint courtship and marriage, literally
give birth to the individual islands of Japan and then to its
mountains, lakes, waterfalls, trees, harbors. Because these islands
and forces of nature are born of divine parents, they themselves
are divine, and then we understand why the Japanese call their
country the "Land of the Gods."

In magnificent panorama the deities continue to throng into
the heavens, earth, and sea. Gradually we begin to realize that
these divinities are infinite in number—"eight hundred myriads of
gods" say the ancient books—for they exist everywhere: in volcanos, rivers, trees, even large rocks or tiny insects. All things are
expressions of divine spirit, and when this vital spirit is unusual
in any way—in size, strength, beauty, shape, color—it is recognized
as a deity, or Kami. An awe-inspiring mountain, a cascading water-

fall, or a river may be Kami. Everything in nature is directed by
deities: there is a goddess to paint the autumn leaves, one to make
the cherry trees blossom, and a sea god to control the waves and
the tide. Some Kami have the form of human beings, but others
are purely spirit, recognized only by their effect on nature itself.

But the beautiful islands do not remain unscarred, for one
of the very divinities who produced this loveliness mars his
own handiwork by bringing forth evil deities. Over all the earth
they swarm, till it is ravaged with discord. Nor is all well in
heaven, for one of the earth-born Kami, the Storm God, ascends a
floating bridge that lies between heaven and earth and comes
into conflict with the Sun Goddess. She is not able to handle
the troublesome deity alone, but being clever she retreats into
a cave, thus bringing about an eclipse that plunges the world
into darkness. Through strategy the eight hundred myriads of
gods lure her out and then banish the Storm God from heaven.

He comes to earth and partially redeems himself—rain and
storm need not be destructive—by rescuing a maiden from a monster and by building up the land. But though he and his descend-

ants rule well, the wicked deities of earth continue to flourish. At length the Sun Goddess sends down her grandson to combat the forces of evil and to establish her own reign on earth. We see the descendant of that grandchild become the first emperor of Japan—the ancestor of all of its 124 emperors to the present day.

The change from the divine being to the human being takes place without a ripple. Man is not created: he simply appears unannounced as a part of the great flowing process of creation. How unlike Greek mythology, with its vivid picture of Prometheus fashioning the first man from clay!

An even greater difference exists between the old stories of Greece and Japan. No one believes in the Greek gods and goddesses any more, though they have become immortalized in our literature, language, science, and arts. The Japanese, on the other hand, still worship their ancient gods, who live on eternally in the forests, mountains, plains, and lakes. To this day when an oil field is being dug or a canal widened, the workers assemble for a ceremonial worship of the spirit of the well or canal; joyous festivals in honor of the gods are frequent; the country is studded with thousands of shrines to the ancient deities. Sometimes these shrines are simple wooden buildings in which are kept symbols of the gods, for Shinto shrines never have images. But a building is quite unnecessary: a mountain stream is in itself evidence of celestial power, and an old tree is sacred simply because it would not be there without the added presence of divine spirit.

To this veneration of nature is added the reverence for one's ancestors as being the gates through which divine spirit has been brought down to the living. In later times historical personages of note were also made gods; thus the number of divinities continues to grow. In no other country have a people's religious beliefs been so closely interwoven with its natural surroundings, daily life, and history.

The wonderful accounts of the creation of Japan and the coming of the gods are found in the nation's two oldest books. The first one, the *Kojiki*, which means "Record of Ancient Matters," gives the story of Japan from the creation to the year 628 A.D. The second book, the *Nihongi*, "Chronicles of Japan," covers the same material but more completely and brings the narrative a little further, up to 700 A.D. Both books were written during the Eighth Century and in Chinese characters, for at that time Japan was deeply influenced by its older and larger neighbor to the west. These are the sacred books of the Japanese. The *Kojiki* in particular has been called the "Bible of Shinto."

Here then are the stories from these sacred texts—stories that take us to the heavens, the earth, the ocean depths, and the underworld. They show us the creation of Japan and of the immortals, the descent of the emperors from the Sun Goddess, and finally the history of the Three Sacred Treasures that to this day are venerated by the Japanese people.

The word "myriad" is ordinarily used to mean a very large, but indefinite number. It can, however, mean an exact number just as the words million and thousand do. A myriad is 10,000.

the creation

Far back in shadowy time there was neither heaven nor earth—
nothing but mists floating through space. Then came a mysterious
stirring, and the mists separated into two parts. One part, light
and transparent, spiraled upward to form the heavens; the other,
heavy and opaque, sank down to become a murky ocean on which
drifted an unformed earth.

Ages passed, and then a miracle occurred. A radiant cloud
glided between heaven and ocean, and from it emerged three
majestic beings: the Lord of the Center of Heaven, the High
Producing God, and the Divine Producing Goddess. Ascending
into the skies, they made the Plain of High Heaven their dwelling
place.

Again a miracle. A reed shoot sprouted on the surface of the
ocean, and from it came two more immortals, the Pleasant Reed
Shoot Prince and the Eternal Sky Stander. Then buds appeared
on the reed shoot, and they brought forth still more deities.

On and on went this miraculous process of divine birth until
seven generations of gods thronged the Plain of High Heaven.
But they were not content, for as yet there was no earth.

The elder deities met in council. "Below us lies a formless
abyss," they said. "Let us send someone down to set it in order."

To their presence they summoned the young god Izanagi and
his companion the goddess Izanami. "A divine task is to be
yours," said the elder deities. "Descend from the skies and solidify
the land that there may be an earth." Then the High Producing

God handed Izanagi a long spear glittering with precious gems and set in a coral staff. "This Sky Jewel Spear will aid you in your work of creation."

Bowing low, Izanagi and Izanami left the assemblage of gods and journeyed to the Floating Bridge of Heaven that hung in splendor between the skies and the ocean below.

From the parapets of the bridge they gazed down in wonder. An alluring fragrance floated up to them from the deep, but they could see nothing except mists curling over, a mottled ocean.

"Could land be hidden in those waters?" asked Izanami. "Earth," she called, "are you there?"

"With the precious treasure given us by the elder deities we must bring the earth into being," said Izanagi.

Leaning far over the edge of the bridge, he thrust the long jeweled spear deep into the ocean and stirred the waters until they seethed into foam. When at length he withdrew the rod, the drops from its tip fell back upon the waves and took form as a tiny island that lay on the sea like an emerald.

"We have caused land to be born from the ocean!" cried Izanagi. "Let us go at once to this lovely place!" Joyously they sped down the Floating Bridge of Heaven to revel in the cool beauty of their islet, which they named Onogoro—"Island of the Congealed Drop."

Entranced with their creation, the celestial pair decided to stay there always. Then they engaged in the ceremony that would make them husband and wife. Setting up the Sky Jewel Spear as a pillar, they walked around the island in opposite directions. When they met, Izanami said, "How delightful! I have found a charming youth!" Gallantly Izanagi replied, "How delightful! I have found a charming maiden!" But then his face clouded. "You have made a mistake. I, the male, should have spoken first. This is an unlucky beginning!"

He was right, for the first child born to them was weak and misshapen. Even at the age of three he could not stand upright. Izanagi put him adrift on the sea in a reed boat, refusing to claim

him as his own. After floating about for a time, the child was transformed into a sea deity. A second child was born to Izanagi and Izanami, but he too was unworthy to be the son of a god; he also was abandoned and drifted away to become a small island.

"Something is wrong," said the unhappy Izanami. "We must consult the elder deities about our misfortunes." Up the Floating Bridge of Heaven the god and goddess traveled. Quickly the stern answer came. "Your children are not good because the maiden spoke first. This is not in accordance with the law of nature. You must go around the pillar again and carry out the rite properly."

Once more the celestial pair descended to their island, set up the pillar, and walked around it. But this time when they met, Izanami kept her eyes demurely down until Izanagi had spoken first: "Ah, what an enchanting maiden!" Then she replied, "Ah, what an enchanting youth!"

And now all was well in their task of creation, for the next children born to them were beautiful and numerous. First they gave birth to the eight large islands of Japan and then to the hundreds of tiny ones that star the surrounding seas. To adorn them the divine couple brought forth mountains, waterfalls, lakes, trees, and flowers, which they arranged in graceful designs.

That nothing should veil this loveliness, Izanagi blew away the mists that still hovered over the land, and from his breath were born the gods of the winds. Then the celestial pair gave birth to deities of seas, plains, harbors, forests, and herbs, so that all nature might share the divine spirit and life.

But the proud parents were not yet satisfied. "If only we could now bring forth a being to rule over the entire universe—a goddess so resplendent that she would give our creations still greater magnificence!"

The wish was fulfilled, for their next child was of surpassing loveliness. "She shall belong to both heaven and earth," decreed Izanagi. As a token of his favor, he placed his own necklace of five hundred jewels about her neck and then took her up the

Floating Bridge to the Plain of High Heaven to reign as the Goddess of the Sun. He named her Amaterasu, which means "Heavenly Light." Under the warmth of her smiles, earth and heaven became even more fair than before.

Then another beautiful child was born. "He too is worthy to dwell in the sky," said the delighted father. "I shall make him the Moon God Tsukiyomi. He shall reign with the Sun Goddess to glorify all things with his silver radiance."

The next child, however, was a rough, blustering deity whom the celestial pair named Susanoo, meaning "Impetuous Male." "His place is definitely on earth," Izanagi decided. "He shall be master of the Great Sea Plain, a domain as restless and turbulent as he himself."

But in the midst of their rejoicing over these innumerable children, sorrow—like a smothering shroud—enveloped the divine parents . . .

It is because of the eight islands born first to the celestial pair that Japan is called "Land of the Eight Great Islands." Actually there are 4,223 isles in the Japanese archipelago, 600 of which are inhabited. It is presumed that the islands when born were small and feeble, reaching their present size by growing just like human children. Because all islands of Japan except Onogoro were offspring of the deities Izanagi and Izanami, they were considered to be divine, other lands having been produced merely from sea foam and mud.

Izanagi means "The Male who Invites"; Izanami means "The Female who Invites." Apparently their lesson that the woman must be the follower, not the initiator, was well learned by the Japanese, for from earliest times women have held an inferior place. Even when walking with her husband, the wife has customarily lagged a short distance behind.

A painting of Izanagi and Izanami peering down from the Floating Bridge of Heaven is in the Museum of Fine Arts in Boston, Massachusetts.

Like Izanagi and Izanami, the creator gods Uranus (you′ rah nus) and Gaea (jee′ ah) in Greek myth also first brought forth strange offspring: hundred-handed Hecatonchires (hek ah ton ky′ reez) and one-eyed Cyclopes (sy klo′ peez). But on the third try both the Japanese and Greek deities redeemed themselves admirably by giving birth to beautiful children.

yomi, land of the dead

The last child that Izanami brought forth was the God of Fire. But in giving birth to him she was cruelly burned, and nothing the devoted Izanagi could do would relieve her suffering. At last she bade him farewell and crept miserably down to Yomi, Land of the Dead. In fury Izanagi slew the Fire God, but from the blood and sword arose eight more deities to join the teeming multitudes now upon the earth.

Izanagi could not endure the loss of Izanami. Night and day his tears fell as raindrops and from them was born the Weeping Rain Deity to sorrow with him. Finally he resolved to travel down to Yomi and bring Izanami back. The way would be hard, but he could meet any obstacle with less suffering than that caused by this grief for his goddess-wife.

A long, toilsome journey brought him to the Pass of Yomi, and he descended into the shadowed caverns of the underworld. Before his eyes stretched a maze of trails winding through endless plains and hills in every direction. Somewhere in that labyrinth was Izanami, but how was he to find her? Patiently he began his search, striding down one purple-misted pathway after another. At last he saw the lofty turrets of a palace cutting through the distant haze. Ah, this must be Izanami's dwelling place! Eagerly he hastened toward it, but as he drew near he saw that the massive doors were guarded by snarling red and black demons. Even a god could not pass that fearsome horde! He must find some other way of entering the palace.

Creeping through the underbrush and circling far to the rear, he came at length upon a small gate. Unseen he slipped through. There in an inner court was his wife, as fair as the day they had stood together on the Floating Bridge of Heaven to create a world.

"I have come to take you back!" he cried. "Without you our beautiful earth holds no joy for me."

Sadly she turned away. "Many days have I yearned for you, my husband. But you have come too late. Having once eaten the food of this land, I can never leave."

"I entreat you to come," he cried. "Can you not find a way?"

Earnestly he pleaded, and at last she said, "Perhaps there is still a chance. Wait here while I seek permission of the gods of Yomi. But do not follow me! Promise that you will not try to see me until I return!" He gave his word, and she went into the palace.

But the time was long. Izanagi grew tired, impatient, and finally very curious. What was keeping her? Why had she forbidden him to enter? He would find out! Breaking a tooth from the comb he wore in the left bunch of his hair, he made it into a torch and entered the palace. A ghastly sight greeted him. His

21

wife had become a swollen, festering corpse surrounded by eight Thunder Deities whose cavernous mouths belched swirls of flame. In terror Izanagi dropped his torch and fled.

Izanami awoke at once. "Why did you not keep your promise?" she cried in dismay. "You have dishonored me with your spying!" Then, realizing that his curiosity had made it impossible for her ever to return to earth, her sorrow turned into vindictive anger. "You shall pay for your disobedience; never shall I let you leave the Land of the Dead!"

Summoning her demon servants, the Eight Ugly Females of Yomi, she shrilled, "Pursue him! Bring him back to me!"

Through the paths of the underworld sped Izanagi, but the swift-footed demons soon were close behind him. He must gain time! Pulling off his headdress, he flung it in their path. At once it was transformed into a bunch of grapes. Greedily the Eight Ugly Females stopped to eat the unaccustomed delicacy, while Izanagi ran on. But again they pursued and again they were nearly upon him, for they were able to leap one thousand miles at a stride. Then he ripped the comb from the right bunch of his hair and cast it at their feet. Instantly it changed into succulent bamboo shoots, which the Females stopped to devour. Seeing this, Izanami became more enraged than ever. "You shall never escape!" she screamed. Then she sent the eight Thunder Deities and fifteen hundred fighting fiends of Yomi after him.

Reeling with exhaustion and fear, but brandishing his ten-length sword defiantly behind him, Izanagi raced on. At the base of a hill leading into the upper passes, he found a peach tree. Plucking its fruit, he flung it so violently at the pursuing demons that they fell back in confusion.

Now Izanami herself took up the furious chase. Just before she caught up with him, he reached the Pass of Yomi and thrust a thousand-man rock* before the entrance. Safe at last!

Storming up to the boulder and stamping with such violence that the underworld shook, the infuriated goddess shrieked, "Why did you break your vow? How could you have so humiliated me whom you love?"

Izanagi had had enough. "From this moment on you are no longer my wife," he called to her from behind the boulder.

"Then I will cause one thousand people to die on earth every day!" she screamed, her anger flaring more wildly than ever.

"But I will cause fifteen hundred to be born every day," he retorted. "Farewell!" Then Izanagi turned his back on her forever.

To purify himself from the pollution of the underworld, he plunged into the pure water at the mouth of a river. But from the staff that he threw down was born a deity; from his sash another; from each of his garments still more, his trousers giving birth to the Road-Fork God. Then he cleansed his body, and from each part of it deities sprang into existence until they

---

*thousand-man rock: a rock that could be lifted by no fewer than a thousand men. You will find other such expressions in this book. Now do you understand "ten-length sword" in the preceding paragraph?

swarmed about him like fireflies on a summer night. Some were good; others, like the Deity of Multiple Calamities, were evil spirits destined to bring endless sorrow and suffering upon gods and men. Thus did Izanagi become the father of his children's enemies.

Izanami returned alone to Yomi, there to become the Great Goddess of the Underworld. Never again was she to see the beautiful land to which she had given birth.

24

The death of the Mother Goddess Izanami marks the beginning of the eternal struggle between life and death that began when the earth was still very young.

It is because of the fiery quarrel and divorce at the Pass of Yomi that there have always been more births than deaths, and thus population has continued to increase through the centuries.

Izanagi's use of peaches to halt his pursuers is indicative of the belief that they are a divine fruit that can ward off evil spirits.

Human hair is considered sacred in Japan and any object connected with it—particularly the comb—takes on a protective quality. Thus Izanagi drew upon supernatural power when he threw his headdress and comb in the path of the demons and also when he used a tooth of his comb as a torch upon entering the palace to seek his wife. Ancient books indicate that in old Japan both men and women wore combs in their hair.

The Eight Thunder Deities represent the underground volcanic rumblings so common in Japan, and the sword that Izanagi brandished behind him as he fled from them is the lightning flash.

Though the differences are many, there are also striking similarities between Japanese and Greek myth. The Greek goddess Persephone (per sef' oh nee) could not leave the underworld because she had eaten of its food, nor could Izanami in faraway Japan. Just as Orpheus (orf' yoose) sought his wife Eurydice (you rid' ee see) in the land of the dead, so did Izanagi; both gods failed because they disobeyed the command, "Don't look!" The titan Prometheus (pro meeth'-yoose) of Greek myth and the Japanese goddess Izanami both give the gift of fire only at the cost of great personal suffering. The Eight Ugly Females of Yomi seem curiously like the Furies of Hades.

the food goddess

The Sun Goddess Amaterasu and the Moon God Tsukiyomi
lived in a radiant palace on the Plain of High Heaven. Together
they flooded the universe with their gold and silver beams, for
Izanagi had commanded them to reign side by side.

One day when they were feasting, Amaterasu—whose appetite
had become a bit jaded—said to her brother, "I have heard that
in the Central Land of Reed Plains below there lives a Food
Goddess who is most clever and inventive. Do you know if the
stories about the foods she produces are true?"

"No, but I shall find out for you at once," replied the Moon
God, always eager to please his beautiful sister.

Passing through crisp new clouds that clustered like plum
blossoms around the Floating Bridge of Heaven, he descended
to earth. He found the home of the Food Goddess and paused
for a few moments under a big tree in her garden to watch her
unobserved, for he had been whisked off to the Plain of High
Heaven so soon after his birth that there had been no chance at
all to see what earth goddesses were like.

When at length he announced himself, Ukemochi received
him graciously, pleased and flattered that an illustrious sky god
should visit her. She decided to place before him the most lavish
of all feasts. In his honor she would even produce tempting new
foods that had never been seen before in heaven or earth.

She turned her face toward land, and from her mouth poured
streams of pearly rice. She turned to the sea, and from her mouth

came fishes of all sorts. She faced the mountains, and game birds and animals issued forth. From these products she prepared hundreds of delectable new dishes and proudly set them before her guest.

Poor Ukemochi! She had not yet had enough experience as a hostess—for after all the world was still very new—to know that trying out new dishes on a guest is always a mistake. Tsukiyomi, far from appreciating her generosity, was insulted. "This is unfit food to offer a god from the Plain of High Heaven!" he fumed. "How dare you serve me with that which came from your mouth!" In his rage he kicked aside the table, drew his sword, and killed Ukemochi.

Storming up to heaven, the hot-tempered Moon God told his sister Amaterasu what had happened. He expected sympathy; he received fiery condemnation. "Wicked, heartless god!" she flamed. "Never again will I welcome you into my presence! No longer will we rule together! Your realm henceforth shall be the night alone!"

She banished him from her sight and never saw him face to face again. Only after the Sun Goddess had left the heavens was the Moon God allowed to venture out.

Deeply grieved over the death of Ukemochi, Amaterasu sent down a sky deity to restore her to life if possible. This he was unable to do, but as he looked at her cold, still body a great marvel took place. Even in death the Food Goddess continued to produce gifts for the benefit of gods and mankind. From her head emerged the horse, cow, and silkworm; from her ears, millet; from her eyes, rice seed. Beans, wheat, and barley poured in rich abundance from other parts of her body.

These gifts were taken to the Plain of High Heaven and placed before the Sun Goddess. Unlike her brother, she could appreciate the worth of such treasures. For each sky village she appointed a head man whom she taught to cultivate the sky fields with the aid of the horse and cow, and then to sow the precious new seeds. Into her own mouth she took the cocoons of the silk-

worm and reeled off thread, thus originating the arts of silk production.

In this manner were the gifts of Ukemochi preserved for all mankind by the gracious Goddess of the Sun.

Japan is dotted with over 100,000 shrines dedicated to the worship of its host of deities. The Geku Shrine in the province of Ise is an important one sacred to the Food Goddess. Closely related to Uke-mochi—and one of the most popular deities—is Inari, God of Rice, whose numerous shrines are characterized by stone images of foxes, Inari's messengers and guardians of the granary.

There are many other deities related to food: gods of the hearth, a kitchen god, a god of the stove, and a god of pots. Giving dignity even to such commonplace things as these kitchen articles is characteristic of the Japanese.

The "Central Land of Reed Plains," by which Japan is referred to in these early myths, is just one of several names attached to this picturesque country. As seen in the Izanagi-Izanami story, it is also known as the "Land of the Eight Great Islands." An emperor in 630 B.C. gave it the name "Land of the Dragon Fly" after viewing it from a lofty mountain and seeing a resemblance to a "dragon fly licking its hinder parts." The Chinese called it "Jih-pen," which means "Land of the Rising Sun," because the islands were east of their own kingdom; our word "Japan" and the Japanese word "Nippon" are corruptions of "Jih-pen." An old Japanese word "Yamato" is still frequently used also. Marco Polo's name for the country was "Zipangu."

In Greek myth there is a sun god Apollo and a moon goddess Artemis (ahr' tee miss). The Japanese reverse the order, making the sun deity a female and the moon deity a male. In both cases they are brother and sister.

Artemis and Dionysus (dy oh ny' suss) gave the Greeks the olive and grape; Ukemochi gave Japan rice, millet, and other food products.

AMATERASU'S MIRROR

Susanoo was a problem. Not only did he refuse to reign as God of the Great Sea Plain as commanded by his father Izanagi, but he often flew into wild tantrums during which he withered the greenery of hills and plains and caused the pretty heads of flowers to droop in despair. Worse still, perhaps, he wept and wailed unceasingly in a manner quite unbefitting a deity, especially one who had an eight-grasp beard that reached to the pit of his stomach!

"Why do you weep?" questioned Izanagi, unable to understand this annoying son.

"Because I wish to go to Yomi where my dead mother Izanami dwells!" sobbed Susanoo.

"Then go!" said the exasperated father. "You really aren't fit to rule the Great Sea Plain anyway. No longer will it be your dominion."

"But wait," insisted Susanoo, drying his tears hastily. "First I must go to the Plain of High Heaven and bid farewell to my sister Amaterasu, Goddess of the Sun." With that he rose into the sky with so much commotion, noise, and bluster that mountains and forests rumbled in earthquake.

Amaterasu, from the sun palace where she and her maidens wove the divine garments of the gods, saw him coming. The thought of this unruly brother invading her well-ordered domain was unbearable. He was sure to destroy or seize it from her! Grimly she prepared her defense.

First she tied her hair into bunches like those of a man. Then she entwined it so thickly with the massive necklace of gems given her by Izanagi before she left earth that the knotted, be-jeweled hair stood up from her head like angry snakes. Next she girded on a glittering sword and slung a thousand-arrow quiver over her back and a five-hundred-arrow quiver from her elbow. Last of all she made a fortification by stamping and kick-ing a hole in the ground with such vigor that the dirt showered about her like a geyser. Thus arrayed as a mighty warrior, she took her stand on the banks of the Tranquil River of Heaven, the Milky Way.

"Halt!" she cried when Susanoo arrived. "Why are you here?"

Susanoo was thoroughly alarmed by these formidable prepara-tions for war, but he pretended to be surprised and hurt. "I have come in peace, dear sister," he protested. "Through cloud and mist I have journeyed up the Floating Bridge of Heaven just to say goodbye before I depart for the Land of Yomi."

"What proof can you give of your good intentions," she asked, still suspicious.

"Let us engage in a god-producing contest," he suggested. "If the deities I bring forth are male, they will be proof of my sincerity and innocence."

"Agreed!" said the goddess. "Hand me your sword."

He tossed it to her across the Tranquil River. She broke it into three pieces, washed the bits in the Heavenly Well, put them in her mouth, and crunched. A rainbow mist swirled from her breath and formed itself into three splendid goddesses.

"And now, your jewels," said Susanoo. From her hair Amaterasu took the string of five hundred gems. He washed them in the Heavenly Well, put them in his mouth, and crunched. Then he exhaled a mist that gave birth to five handsome gods.

"See!" he exclaimed triumphantly. "The children that came from my breath are all males because my heart is pure!"

"But of course they are really my children," said Amaterasu sweetly, "for they were produced from jewels that belonged to me." However, convinced of her brother's good intentions and pleased with the deities he had brought forth, she welcomed him into her kingdom.

But Susanoo could not behave himself long. His old mischievous nature soon revealed itself, and very shortly the Sun Goddess discovered that he was wantonly tearing down her rice fields, breaking her irrigation ditches, and strewing noxious seeds throughout the land. At harvest time he even loosed a herd of colts into the fields to ruin the crop. At first she excused his misdeeds, but her patience only incited him to bolder destruction.

Finally he subjected her to a most unforgivable indignity. As she and her maidens were weaving in the great hall and celebrating the Feast of First Fruits, he ripped open the roof and flung a dead horse into their midst. The maidens screamed in horror. Amaterasu wounded herself with her shuttle, and her younger sister Princess Weaving pierced herself so violently that she died.

The Sun Goddess could endure no more. Outraged, she left her radiant palace and hid herself in a deep cave, the Heavenly

Rock Dwelling. Thus deprived of her shining presence, sky and earth were plunged into gloom. Unending night fell; evil spirits rampaged unchecked through the earth; trees, flowers, and grasses drooped.

Consternation swept the Plain of High Heaven, and the eight hundred myriads of gods thronged to the cave and begged Amaterasu to come out. But to all their pleas she replied, "I have been grossly insulted. Here I shall remain forever."

The distressed deities met in council. "Since we cannot persuade her to emerge from the cave, we must' resort to trickery," said the High Producing God.

"I suggest that we take advantage of her natural woman's curiosity," said another.

They devised a plan and set to work. The Heavenly Smith welded stars into a gleaming mirror to represent the brightness of the sun. The Jewel Ancestor made an eight-foot string of curved, comma-shaped jewels. Then a five-hundred-branched tree from the Fragrant Sky Mountain was placed before the cave and bedecked with the mirror, the gems, and streamers of blue and white cloth. The Thought Combining God brought birds from the Eternal Land, and crowing cocks were set before the cave to remind the sulking goddess that it was time for the sun to rise.

Then the eight hundred myriads of gods held a great celebration, which was climaxed with a thumping, merry dance on a hollow tub by the plump little goddess Uzume. Gayer and gayer became the party, until the Plain of High Heaven rang with the sounds of merriment.

Inside the cave, Amaterasu was at first amazed and then insulted. How could the deities be happy when she, Goddess of the Sun, was not with them! A cock crowed, as though there could be daybreak without her! She became intolerably curious. Whatever was producing all that rollicking good cheer? She would take one quick look and find out. Opening the door a crack, she asked, "Why do you laugh?"

"Because we have found a more beautiful goddess than you," one deity replied.

"Impossible!" said Amaterasu.

Then the deity held the mirror before her eyes. There indeed was an exquisite maiden! Captivated, Amaterasu emerged a bit farther for a closer view of the enchanting creature. Instantly the God of Force pulled her out, while another deity drew a rope behind her to prevent a retreat into the cave. One especially strong god seized the stone door and flung it to earth, where it still rests on Mount Tsukuba. And now heaven and earth were again flooded with brilliant sunshine.

The eight hundred myriads of gods punished Susanoo by imposing a heavy fine, cutting off his beard, and expelling him from the Plain of High Heaven that he might never again offend the glorious Goddess of the Sun.

34

The Ise Shrine houses the sacred mirror that drew Amaterasu from the cave. During ceremonies the goddess's spirit enters into it and listens to the prayers addressed to her. In the grounds of the shrine are cocks, sacred to the sun because they salute the dawn. Torii, picturesque gates at Shinto shrines, are believed to represent the roost of the cocks that crowed before the cave. "Mirror cakes" are eaten at the New Year Festivals.

The eight deities produced by Amaterasu and Susanoo were worshipped as the ancestors of Japan's royal families, the eldest deity being the ancestor of the emperor himself.

Uzume, whose thumping little dance helped to create the laughter that enticed Amaterasu from the cave, is the Goddess of Dancing and Cheer. Her special dance, Kagura, meaning "god music," is an important part of Shinto ceremonials. She was the first geisha, or dancing girl, of Japan; modern geisha costumes are often modeled after hers.

The Feast of the First Fruits that Amaterasu was celebrating when Susanoo offended her is still observed in Japan each fall.

The Sun Goddess enchanted by her own reflection in a mirror is reminiscent of the youth Narcissus (nar siss' us) who, in Greek myth, fell in love with his image in a woodland pool.

the eight-forked serpent

After the eight hundred myriads of gods had banished Susanoo from the Plain of High Heaven, he descended to the Central Land of Reed Plains beside the River Hi. Seeing a chopstick floating on the water, he knew that people were near. A bit lonely and dejected after all the excitement he had caused in heaven, he set out to find the people. Soon he came upon an old man, an old woman, and a maiden—all weeping distractedly. As it was a novelty to find anyone who could weep as profusely as he, Susanoo became interested at once.

"Who are you, and why do you weep?" he asked the old man.

"I am an earthly deity, as is my wife," was the reply. "We have had eight daughters, but each year an eight-forked serpent has devoured one. Now the time has come for him to take our last child!"

"What is this serpent like?" asked Susanoo, noting that the girl was very fair. Food for a serpent? Such a waste!

"He has eight heads, eight tails, and eyes red as a winter cherry," moaned the old man. "His body stretches over eight hills and valleys, and moss and cypress trees grown on his thorny back!"

Susanoo looked again at the maiden. No doubt about it: she was much too pretty for that ugly monster. Then he drew himself up proudly.

"I, the brother of the Sun Goddess, will save your daughter if you will give her to me in marriage."

"Oh yes!" cried the old man, "Save her and she is yours!"

Quickly Susanoo transformed the girl into a comb, which he thrust into his hair. "Distill some wine," he ordered the old couple. "Then build a circular fence with eight gates, each with its own platform, and on every one place a tub of wine."

The old couple scurried about to do his bidding. Scarcely had they completed the task when a mighty rumbling of the earth heralded the coming of the monster.

"Hide!" commanded Susanoo. Then he concealed himself in such a position that his image was reflected in each tub.

Slithering over hills and valleys that shuddered in horror beneath him, the monster made his way to the gates. His eyes were like scorching suns, his breath a sizzling wind. For a moment he snorted about impatiently and then thrust one scaly head into a tub of wine. In its shining surface he saw the reflection of the concealed Susanoo and mistook it for the girl. A nice morsel, this! Greedily he gulped down the liquid. She was gone, and there was nothing left in his mouth! Puzzled, he put a head into the next tub. Ah, here she was!

Again he drank; again frustration! Hissing furiously now, he thrashed from tub to tub, finding—and yet not finding—her in

every one. But the wine had begun to do its work, and by the time his eighth head had dipped into the eighth tub more than one maiden seemed to be peering up at him.

The flaming eyes began to close, the horny heads to weave. Down he sprawled at last in a drunken sleep.

Up sprang Susanoo from his hiding place and began to hack at the serpent with his ten-grasp saber. The sinuous body writhed in convulsions that shook the ground like an earthquake, and the deity had to skip nimbly to avoid those jerking tails and heads.

Busily he slashed away until the River Hi turned crimson with blood, and neat chunks of fresh serpent were piled along its banks. But when he brought down his saber on the last tail, the weapon rebounded with a clang, broken in two. This was no ordinary tail! Probing about in it with the severed point of his saber, Susanoo at length dug out a magnificent eight-grasp sword.

"This is a divine weapon," he told the old couple, who had been watching his afternoon's work with rapt admiration. He eyed it thoughtfully for a few moments, and then came to a decision. "I shall give it to the Sun Goddess Amaterasu," he declared, feeling, no doubt, that he owed her something.

Then Susanoo transformed the comb in his hair back into the maiden. She seemed even more beautiful than before, especially after those eight serpent heads he had just chopped off.

"So enchanting a maid should be married in the choicest part of the Central Land of Reed Plains. Come, let us find such a place."

Together the deity and the maiden wandered about until they same to a softly wooded spot where earth and sky were bathed in a fragrant, golden mist. "Here shall we be wed," cried Susanoo, "for here my heart feels refreshed."

Fascinated particularly by the wind-spun clouds hovering over the tree tops, he praised them in song, and in their honor named the area "Izumo," which means "rising clouds." Then he built a palace in this delightful place for the maiden whom he had won so gallantly with the blood of an eight-forked serpent.

But the old wanderlust returned, and he traveled to the limits of the earth and did great deeds. In time he went down to the underworld as, long ago, he had told his father Izanagi and his sister Amaterasu that he intended to do. There he reigned as one of its most important deities.

Behind him in Izumo his numerous children multiplied and flourished. In the sixth generation came his most important descendant, the god Okuninushi.

There are many shrines to Susanoo in Izumo Province. The Great Shrine of Kitsuki is particularly important because here the deities of Japan assemble on the first day of October to arrange all marriages for the coming year. This assembly of gods takes place at four o'clock in the morning; people are careful to stay indoors so as not to disturb the deities in their matchmaking. In actual life "go-betweens" carry out these decrees of the gods, young people ordinarily not choosing their own mates. October is known as the "godless month" in all parts of the country except Izumo, since all the deities come there for the great marriage conclave.

Susanoo's slaying of the eight-forked serpent is pictured on Japan's paper currency, and the sword has been revered down through the centuries as one of the empire's three most sacred treasures.

okuninushi

Along one of Izumo's reed-bordered pathways came eighty deities, descendants of Susanoo. They were brothers, all journeying to Inaba to seek the hand of the Princess Yakami. Far behind them trudged the patient young deity Okuninushi, their youngest brother whom they had brought along to carry their luggage.

The day was hot and the luggage heavy. As a result, Okuninushi had fallen far to the rear, when he came upon a poor little hare huddled miserably in the bushes. Every inch of his fur coat had been stripped off, and the pink skin had become so shrunken and dry that there was hardly room for his body inside of it. Sadly the hare told his story to the sympathetic Okuninushi.

"A flood came to the bamboo grove where I was born and washed it far out to the island of Oki. There I was, alone and homesick, with no way to get back to the mainland. Ah, but I am smart, and I worked out a plan. Cultivating the acquaintance of a crocodile that used to lounge at the water's edge, I said to him one day, 'It's a great comfort to be a member of a large tribe; my people number hundreds.'

" 'So do mine,' said the crocodile.

" 'I don't believe it,' I said. 'I shall have to be convinced; no one belongs to so large a family as I.'

" 'Meet me here tomorrow,' said the crocodile, 'and I shall have all my relatives assembled so that you may count them.'

"The next morning there they were, hundreds of them, in a line so long that it stretched from the island right to the front

yard of my home. I leaped upon their backs and, counting loudly, skipped from one to another. But just as I was about to jump to shore, I made a mistake. 'Silly creatures,' I said. 'What do I care how many crocodiles there are! I only wanted to get across the water.' At that a big burly rascal whipped up his snout and relieved me of my white coat.

"I was in bad trouble, but it got worse when eighty wicked deities came by a short while ago and, pretending to be my friend, advised me to bathe in the salty sea and then lie in the wind. I did, and now my woes are more than I can bear!" The little hare wept, and the salty tears dripping down his skinned cheeks made him more wretched than ever.

"Poor fellow!" said Okuninushi. "Bathe in a fresh water stream and roll in the herbs by its banks; then you will be healed. Here, I will help you."

The hare did as he was told and was soon his tricky self again.

"Because of your kindness, you shall win the Princess Yakami," he predicted.

And he was right. The princess would have none of the eighty brothers. "I shall wed only the one who was kind to the skinned hare," she declared.

The brothers were furious. "Okuninushi shall pay with his life for this!" and their eighty heads began to churn with evil plans.

Being extraordinary deities, they came up with extraordinary ideas. Insisting that Okuninushi return to Izumo with them although he much preferred the company of the princess to whom he had just been betrothed, they led him to a high mountain. "There is a red boar here," they told him. "Catch it without fail or you shall die!"

They built a fire, heated a boar-shaped boulder, and rolled it down the slope where their brother was searching. Bravely he sprang forward to battle what he thought to be a ferocious creature crashing down upon him. He caught it and was burned to death.

Now his mother possessed a magic mirror that enabled her to see things far beyond the normal range of vision. Peering into it, she saw her youngest son's charred body lying at the foot of the mountain. Up to the Plain of High Heaven she hastened and appealed to the Divine Producing Goddess to restore Okuninushi to life. "Princess Cockle Shell and Princess Clam can do this job best," said the deity. "They shall help you."

Down the Floating Bridge of Heaven came the two princesses. One of them crushed her cockle shells into a fine powder, which she roasted. The other mixed it with water. With this salve they bathed Okuninushi and restored his burned body to life.

The eighty brothers were more angry than ever and again sought to kill Okuninushi, this time by imprisoning him in the wedge of a tree. Once more his mother's mirror showed her where he was. Chopping the tree in half, she released him from the cruel trap and coaxed life back into his bruised body.

"Now this just can't go on forever," she told him. "Flee to Yomi, the underworld. Only there will you be safe."

Not at all curious to find out what his brothers would do to him next, Okuninushi started off at once. He had traveled only a short distance when they saw him and started in wild pursuit. By darting back and forth among trees through which the arrows of his brothers fell like autumn leaves in a whirlwind, Okuninushi escaped down into the dark Pass of Yomi.

At first it wasn't nearly so gloomy down there as he had expected, for he soon met a princess, Suseri-Hime, who promptly fell in love with him and offered to introduce him to her father Susanoo, deity of the underworld. Then came the gloom, for when she announced, "A handsome god has arrived," her father said, "Make him sleep in the Snake House!"

The princess had to obey this inhospitable command, but as Okuninushi entered the dreadful room she slipped a silk scarf under his arm. "When the snakes come," she whispered, "wave this at them three times." It hardly seemed an appropriate weapon to use against snakes, but as she offered nothing better, he had to be satisfied.

No sooner had he lain down to rest than the walls began to quiver and squirm. Thousands of snakes were slithering toward him from every side! So swiftly did they come that they were almost upon him before he remembered the scarf. He waved it. Abruptly the creatures recoiled upon their tails and tumbled back into the walls.

Early the next morning the deity himself came to unlock the door. He seemed disappointed to find his guest in good condition. Then he brightened and said cheerfully, "Tonight you shall enjoy more of our hospitality. You shall sleep in the House of Centipedes and Wasps!"

But this time Okuninushi did not worry, feeling sure that the princess would produce another scarf. She did, but he nearly had troubles anyway: the creatures descended upon him like a tidal wave, and he was nearly drowned in a sea of legs, wings, and stingers before he could free a hand and brandish the wisp of silk.

The third test of Okuninushi's courage offered more variety,
for Susanoo next shot an arrow into a vast moor and commanded,
"Bring back my arrow before nightfall!"

Out went the young god to search among the reeds, but he
soon found that flames were dancing up in all directions. The
deity had set fire to the moor! No escape seemed possible this
time, for the princess had neglected to come forth with a scarf.

Then, above the crackling of the flames, Okuninushi heard an
imperious squeak. Looking down he saw an excited little field
mouse scurrying back and forth, obviously beseeching him to
follow her. To a deep hole she led him, and there he rested
until the flames had passed. The tiny creature then frisked back
with the arrow in her mouth and proudly dropped it at his feet.

Susanoo received the arrow in silence: this was no ordinary god who had come to his dominions! Perhaps he should be used rather than abused. "Come into the palace and wash the centipedes out of my hair," he commanded sourly. Okuninushi obeyed, reflecting that the deity's plans were becoming progressively less interesting and worthy of him.

Having his hair washed was apparently soothing to Susanoo's ruffled spirits, for in a few moments he had fallen sound asleep, perhaps to dream up more tests for his uninvited guest.

But Okuninushi was tired of his visit. Besides, some new ideas had begun to skip around in his head. Still pretending to wash the hair, he tied it securely to the rafters. Then he took Princess Suseri-Hime on his back, tucked Susanoo's sword, bow, and heavenly speaking flute under his arm, and fled. All went well until the flute brushed against some trees and sent up a plaintive wail that awakened the deity.

Bristling with rage, Susanoo sprang to his feet and lunged toward the door. His body was jerked back like a whiplash! The feet would go but the head wouldn't follow! Whirling about to face his unseen enemy, he howled with pain as great tufts of hair were ripped from his head. He strained and thrashed and flailed about in a frenzy, but each move only brought new agonies. Finally the whole palace tumbled down about his aching head, and he was able to unfasten the knots that bound his hair. After the fleeing god and princess he thundered, but by that time they had reached the Pass of Yomi.

Seeing himself defeated, and struck by a grudging admiration, Susanoo shouted to Okuninushi, "You've eluded me, villain! Now pursue your eighty brothers, whose jealousies cause such endless disturbance. Sweep them before you with my sword and bow! Make yourself master of the land, with my daughter as your wife!" At least one member of the family was to get something useful out of that upstart god's visit to the underworld!

Okuninushi followed these instructions. The sword and bow of Susanoo proved to be powerful weapons. With them he scourged the eighty wicked brothers up hills, through valleys, over cliffs, and into rivers, until they howled for mercy and promised submission. Then Okuninushi established himself as the Great Land Master, ruler of Izumo, and began to establish peace and order in the realm.

Susanoo had two souls, a wicked one that prompted him to do evil and a peaceful one that prompted him to do good.

The Japanese do not have a man in the moon, but instead they see the White Hare of Inaba. Patiently he sits up there, pounding rice-cake in a mortar. The hare is also one of the twelve zodiac signs.

In Japanese myth the hare in general is credited with supernatural powers and is said to live a thousand years, its hair becoming white after the first five hundred.

The dwarf god has in modern times become one of the most popular deities in Japan, being revered as the father of medicine. He is still believed to appear on earth to lead sick people to curative waters. Thus he is often called "God of the Hot Springs." He is also credited with being the master of charms and incantations to cure illness, and is supposed to be the inventor of the art of brewing *sake,* or rice wine.

Okuninushi is the Japanese Earth God. As such, he is identified with the God of Wealth, because the earth is the original source of all riches. Further, as the healer of the White Hare of Inaba and a companion of the dwarf god, he is associated with the arts of medicine and magic.

the dwarf god

One day as Okuninushi, the Great Land Master, was traveling through his domain, he heard a voice that seemed to come from the ocean. At first he could see nothing. Then he caught sight of a boat no larger than a bean pod coming in from the waters.

Although it bounced steadily over the waves as if guided by an expert hand, it seemed to have nothing in it. But as it came closer, he saw that it carried a little dwarf god clad in moth wings and a mantle of feathers.

Delighted with the wee fellow, Okuninushi took him in his hand. Instantly the dwarf god sprang up and bit him on the cheek in warning that he was not to be trifled with.

"What is your name?" asked Okuninushi, regarding his visitor with greater respect. No answer.

Deities, animals, and birds had by this time crowded around to see the newcomer. "Do any of you know who he is?" inquired Okuninushi. All shook their heads. Then the scarecrow, Crumbling Prince, pushed his way in. "Why, this is Prince Little Renown," he said, "child of the Divine Producing Goddess."

Okuninushi promptly sent messengers to the Plain of High Heaven to see if this were so. The Divine Producing Goddess looked thoughtful for a moment and then said, "Tell the Great Land Master that I have produced fifteen hundred children. One of these, Prince Little Renown, was born from the fork of my hand. The mischievous creature slipped away one night, and I haven't seen him since. That must be the child who came sailing

over the sea to Izumo. Tell Okuninushi to love him like a brother and to let him help develop and rule the land."

"Help me! One so tiny as he? Why, he can't even walk yet!" laughed the Great Land Master.

"Ah, but he is smart," said Crumbling Prince.

Okuninushi soon discovered that the scarecrow was right, for Prince Little Renown knew everything—how to cure wounds and diseases, how to cultivate useful plants, and how to make evil deities behave. Working together as brothers, the big god of the Central Land of Reed Plains and the diminutive god from the Plain of High Heaven made the earth a more pleasant place than ever.

Prince Little Renown worked much too hard for one so small, however, and in time he became quite ill. Okuninushi was deeply distressed, having learned to love his wee helper. To cure him, the deity brought hot water in underground pipes from a distant spring and bathed the dwarf god. The little fellow revived, jumped up, and skipped happily about on the surface of the water that had relieved his pain. His footprints have remained on the spring ever since.

But Okuninushi eventually lost his friend and helper after all, for one day Prince Little Renown climbed an ear of millet to see if it was ripening properly. The slender stalk swayed and then rebounded: into the air sailed the tiny god, so far and so long that he never found his way back. Yet the useful arts he had taught were never forgotten but lived on forever to bless the lives of gods and men.

the heavenly grandson

48   After Okuninushi had ruled for a long time, the Sun Goddess
Amaterasu became highly discontented with the state of affairs
on earth. She had not forgotten the unruly conduct of her brother
Susanoo when he had visited her on the Plain of High Heaven.
It was not fitting, she decided, that his descendants should rule
the Central Land of Reed Plains. She would send her own son,
one of the gods born from her jewels in the contest with Susanoo,
to take Okuninushi's place.

At first the son was delighted with the idea of descending to
earth, and he peered down from the Floating Bridge of Heaven
with great interest at the realm that his goddess mother offered
him. But soon he discovered that it was full of disturbances.
Despite the hard work of Okuninushi and Prince Little Renown,
earth was not yet like heaven. The evil spirits born from Izanagi's
purifying bath after his return from the underworld had multiplied and now swarmed like fireflies over the land. Even the
rocks, trees, and herbs—which at this time still had the power of
speech—were riotous and noisy. "Why should I leave the peaceful
Plain of High Heaven for such a place as this?" said the deity
disdainfully, and back he went to the quiet and comfort of his
sky dwelling.

Then the Sun Goddess called the eight hundred myriads of
gods together in council. To the God Who Hoards Thoughts she
said, "Can you devise a plan for stopping the disorders on earth,
so that it may become fit for a ruler from the heavens?"

"Let a messenger be sent first to see just what is happening down there," he suggested.

The deity Sky Great Sun was appointed to the task. But he failed to return, so great was his admiration for Okuninushi. After three years the sky deity's son was sent to find him, but the son did not come back either. A third messenger fell in love with Okuninushi's daughter and after eight years still had not reported back to the eight hundred myriads of gods.

Exasperated and insulted that her messengers could forget their duties to heaven, Amaterasu sent down her two best generals to demand that Okuninushi surrender the Central Land of Reed Plains to the Sun Goddess.

Reluctantly the Great Land Master agreed to yield to the heavenly envoys on condition that he and his descendants should still have control over the hidden mysteries of medicine and magic that he had been taught by the dwarf god Prince Little Renown. But Okuninushi's second son was unwilling to relinquish the land. "Let us submit to a trial of strength," he suggested.

For answer, one of the heavenly envoys thrust out his hand and the son took it. The hand became first an icicle and then a sharp blade in the son's grasp. In turn the son extended his hand, and the sky deity crushed it like a dry reed.

"You win," said the Great Land Master, "We will give up our realm to the Goddess of the Sun."

In the meantime, Amaterasu had decided that her favorite grandson Ninigi was the proper deity to establish her rule in the Central Land of Reed Plains. Summoning him into her radiant presence, she gave him three precious gifts: the divine sword that Susanoo had ripped from the tail of the eight-forked serpent, the star-mirror that had enticed her from the cave, and her necklace of jewels. "Guard these treasures as emblems of your divine power," she told him. "Revere especially the mirror: look upon it as though it were I. Let it be with you in your palace and on your couch. Do this, and the prosperity of you and your descendants as divine rulers shall be as everlasting as heaven and earth."

Thus laden with divine treasures, Ninigi and a resplendent
company of deities to serve him began their descent to earth.
Hardly had they broken through the clouds, however, when their
way was blocked by a giant with a nose five feet long and eyes
so piercing and brilliant that they seemed almost to scorch the
heavenly party. Ninigi and his companions shrank back in alarm.
But the merry little goddess Uzume, she who had danced before
Amaterasu's cave, stepped indignantly up to the giant and demanded, "Who are you that dares to bar the way of the Sun
Goddess's grandson whom she has sent to rule the Central Land
of Reed Plains?"

"I am the Deity of the Field Paths," replied the giant, his eyes becoming even brighter at the sight of the bewitching little goddess from the sky. "I ask the privilege of being your master's guide."

"Your services are accepted," said Ninigi, coming forward hastily, a bit embarrassed that the winsome Goddess of Dance should have been braver than he.

Down the Floating Bridge of Heaven the sky deities continued their journey to earth, alighting at last on a lofty mountain. Then, guided by the Deity of Field Paths, Ninigi explored the land. On Cape Kasasa, where the sunshine was especially bright, the giant built a palace befitting the Heavenly Grandson, first of the Sun Goddess's descendants to reign upon the earth.

51

Well did he rule. In time the power of the evil spirits was checked and the clamorous voices of tree, herb, and rock were silenced forever.

The dauntless Uzume fell in love with the giant who looked so fierce but behaved so gently, and one day she became his bride.

Because Amaterasu overthrew the descendants of Susanoo and established her rule on earth, she became the most important of all Shinto deities. This worship of the Sun Goddess is symbolized in the national flag of Japan, which pictures a rising sun.

The Floating Bridge of Heaven, so long the passageway of the gods between heaven and earth, collapsed one day when all the deities were asleep. It fell to earth and formed a stony cape in the province of Tango.

Mount Kirishima on the island of Kyushu is especially sacred to the Japanese because on its eastern peak, Takachiho, the god Ninigi descended to establish the rule of the Sun Goddess.

Japanese artists find humor in the incident of Uzume and the giant, and they enjoy depicting her as stroking his five-foot-long nose.

The shrines of Okuninushi, great deity of Izumo, are visited by thousands of worshippers, sometimes heaven itself becoming temporarily empty because all the gods have assembled on earth to honor him.

the princess who makes
the flowers to bloom

52   Journeying one day through the Central Land of Reed Plains,
Ninigi saw in the distance a majestic mountain. He hastened
to it and stood in admiration at its base. Not even the Fragrant
Sky Mountain of heaven was lovelier than this. In solitary splendor it rose from the midst of a plain, its snow-capped cone like
an immense inverted fan. Gentle slopes were clothed in forests
and moorlands, and a fragrant grove lay at its feet.

Wending his way into the grove, Ninigi came upon a maiden
as beautiful as those who graced the palace of the Sun Goddess.
At first glance he was captivated.

"Who are you?" he asked.

"I am the Princess Who Makes The Flowers To Bloom and
also the Goddess of this fair Mount Fuji," she answered.

"And your father?"

"He is the deity Great Mountain Possessor."

To the deity went Ninigi, determined to have the princess for
his bride.

Now the Great Mountain Possessor was delighted with the
prospect of getting so distinguished a son-in-law, but he had
another daughter, Princess Long As The Rocks, whose face was
as strange as her name. "This is my other treasure. Take her as
your wife," he urged, eager to find a husband for the older daughter first.

"No," said Ninigi, "I will wed only the maiden whom I met
in the grove."

Princess Long As The Rocks was hurt and angry. "If you had taken me, you and your children would have lived long in the land and should have had life as eternal as the rocks. Now that you have chosen my sister, you shall perish as quickly as cherry blossoms."

Ninigi paid no attention to these gloomy predictions but married the princess of his choice. For a while he was very happy with his young bride. But in time jealousy crept into his heart and began to torment him night and day. Try as she would, the princess could not convince her husband that his suspicions were unfounded. Life became dismal, and her pretty head drooped like a fading chrysanthemum.

Finally she could endure her unhappiness no longer. Going into a small wooden hut, she said to Ninigi, "I shall set fire to this place. If I am innocent, my child who is about to be born will not perish. Then you will know."

Flames crackled and rolled, and the hut was consumed. But from its ashes emerged three baby boys, unharmed.

Ninigi named one of them Hoderi, "Fire Shine," and another one Hoori, "Fire Fade." Tenderly he cherished them. What happened to the third little boy, "Fire Climax," no one seems to know.

The Princess Who Makes The Flowers To Bloom is worshipped at a spring at the foot of Mount Fuji. Her shrine, which has existed from time immemorial, is in the midst of a grove of wild cherry trees, and it is she who produces their delicate blossoms. As goddess of the mountain, she has a shrine on the summit, to which white-clad pilgrims have climbed for hundreds of years. Many legends associate this shrine with the Elixir of Life, a magic nectar that imparts immortality and eternal youth. The emperor of China is said to have sent a hundred young men and women to bring back the nectar. They never returned: once having seen beautiful Japan, they could not bear to leave.

The words of Princess Long As The Rocks came true. Because Ninigi chose the younger sister, he and his descendants—the emperors of Japan—have lived as briefly as other people, despite their descent from the Sun Goddess.

hoori and
the dragon princess

As Ninigi's children, the gods Hoderi and Hoori, were growing up, it became apparent that each had been given a special
gift. Hoderi was so skillful as a fisherman that he always returned
with a loaded boat, and Hoori's arrows never seemed to miss their
mark as he roamed the hills in search of game.

One day after returning from the hunt, Hoori said to his
brother, "Doing exactly the same thing all the time becomes
tiresome. Why do we not exchange occupations for just one day?
Tomorrow you take my bow and hunt in the mountains while I
try my luck with your fishhook in the sea."

"No!" replied the elder brother. "Never will I give up my
precious fishhook."

"Ah, but you would love the sound and feel of my feathered
arrows as they sing through the mountain air," wheedled Hoori.
"Please, just for one day." He coaxed so long and eloquently
that Hoderi at last consented. "But take care of my fishhook," he
warned; "there is no other one like it in the world."

Hoori, delighted to have a new experience, took his boat far out
to sea where he believed the fish would be most numerous. But
to his disappointment he had no luck whatever. Not one living
creature came near all day long. Then just as he was ready to
give up and go home, something tugged at his line. He drew
it in; there was a snap, and the fishhook was gone!

Meanwhile Hoderi had tramped the hills and forests from
morning till night without catching even a glimpse of a bird or

animal. Tired and annoyed, he vowed never again to waste time on so dull an occupation as hunting. He could hardly wait to get his magic fishhook into his hands again.

When he arrived home, he found his brother Hoori sitting on the shore staring out to sea. "I have had no fun at all today,"

grumbled Hoderi. "Take your old bow and arrows and give me my fishhook."

"I cannot; it is lost!" confessed Hoori miserably.

Hoderi's anger flared into the fury of a volcano. Brushing aside all pleas for forgiveness he shouted, "Find my precious fishhook again! Find it! None other will ever replace it!"

All night long Hoori sat on the beach, cutting his splendid sword into small pieces and twisting them into fishhooks. Day after day he worked until he had made five hundred to present to his brother. Surely one of them would be acceptable. But Hoderi tossed them aside scornfully and again demanded, "Find my *own* fishhook!"

Then the disconsolate Hoori began to spend all his time pacing up and down the shore, hoping that somehow the lost object

would be cast upon the sands. One afternoon an old man stopped him and said, "I have been watching you for a long while. What can I, the Lord of the Tide, do to help the son of the Heavenly Grandchild?"

"Show me how to find my brother's fishhook!" Hoori cried, pouring out the whole sad story.

"That is too big a job for me," said the Lord of the Tide. "Only the Sea God can help. But I will show you how to reach his kingdom." Taking a black comb from his bag, he tossed it on the ground. Immediately it became a clump of bamboo, which the old man wove into a basket.

"This will carry you down through the waters to a pleasant pathway leading to a palace that appears to be built of fish scales. When you reach the gates, you will see a cassia tree. Climb into its branches and wait there until someone from the palace discovers you."

The eager Hoori stepped into the basket and was swiftly borne down through the misty sea lanes to a splendid palace. By the shining gates he saw a cassia tree, its graceful branches reflected in a clear well beneath. Climbing into the tree, Hoori waited as he had been instructed. Soon a little maidservant came to draw water. There in the well she saw the image of the handsome young god. Smiling down at her, Hoori said, "Please give me a drink." When she handed him a cup, he placed a rich jewel in it.

Bubbling with excitement, the maid fluttered into the palace and soon returned with her mistress Toyotama, daughter of the Sea God. The princess and the youth gazed into each other's eyes, and suddenly the whole ocean seemed to sparkle.

She led him to her father, who recognized him at once as the son of the Heavenly Grandchild. "We are honored by your visit," said the Sea God. Then he ordered his servants to prepare a couch of eight layers of sealskins and eight layers of silk and to place delicacies from the eight corners of the sea before Hoori. The princess stayed close by to keep his wine cup filled, and soon all the servants—from the dignified carp to the giggling little gold-fish—were whispering that their mistress and the youth had fallen in love.

The Sea God, pleased to have his daughter marry a descendant of the glorious Amaterasu, gave them a magnificent wedding. Then for three years Hoori was so happy with his princess that not even a sigh for home and earth escaped his lips.

But gradually he began to remember his promise to return the fishhook. A worried little frown perched on his forehead and refused to go away. Learning the cause of his distress, the Sea God called all the fishes of the ocean together and asked if any

of them had seen the fishhook. One matronly old mackerel spoke up and said, "The tai has had a sore throat for a long time and thus could not come today. Perhaps it is that fishhook that is bothering him." She was right. The ailing tai was brought to the palace, and in his mouth was the long-lost object.

Hoori was jubilant. "Let me take it to my brother and then I shall return to this kingdom to stay forever." The Sea God could not refuse his request, though the princess grieved bitterly at the thought of losing her beloved husband even for a short time.

"Take these two jewels," said the Sea God. "The blue one is the Jewel of the Flowing Tide, the white one the Jewel of the Ebbing Tide. If your brother is kind and forgiving, you will not need them. If he is still angry, use them to defend yourself."

Then the sorrowing princess came to bid him farewell. "Our child is about to be born," she said, "and it is fitting that a descendant of the Sun Goddess be brought forth on earth rather than in the kingdom of the sea. I shall come to you on the shore. Watch for me on a day when winds and waves are raging."

Mounting a dragon in the shape of a crocodile, Hoori sped through the waters up to earth and sought his brother. But the rage that had smoldered during the years that Hoderi had been without his fishhook leaped into flame when he saw Hoori. "Wretch!" he cried. "How dared you wait so long!" With sword upraised he bore down upon his younger brother.

Hoori brought forth the Jewel of the Rising Tide. Swirling waves thundered in from the sea and engulfed Hoderi in a tempestuous flood. "Save me, brother!" gasped the drowning god.

Then Hoori tossed the Jewel of the Ebbing Tide into the waters, and they raced back to their ocean home. "I and all my descendants forever will be your loyal servants," said the elder brother gratefully, humbled by this evidence of Hoori's strange new powers.

Now Hoori's thoughts turned to his sea princess. On the shore he built for her a house roofed with cormorant feathers and then waited eagerly for the tossing winds and waves that would herald her ascent from the sea kingdom. True to her promise, she came. But before entering the house she turned to him imploringly: "I beseech you, do not try to see me again until our child is born. Give me your solemn vow!"

"It shall be as you wish," he replied.

Patiently he waited outside for a long time, becoming more and more curious every moment about her request. Finally, unable to restrain himself any longer, he peered into the hut. Horror-stricken he recoiled: his wife had turned into a dragon eight fathoms long!

As soon as her child was born, the princess became again the beautiful maiden with whom Hoori had been so enchanted. But she felt dishonored because her husband had seen her in dragon form. "I must leave you now and close the sea lanes between us forever. No longer will there be easy communication between ocean and land. Farewell!" Then, wrapping her baby in rushes and placing him tenderly on the shore, she slipped into the water and was gone. Never again would she see the husband she loved so well.

But though she wished her child to stay in the land of his father, she could not abandon him. Soon she sent her younger sister from the sea palace to be his nurse.

When this child grew up, he married and had four children. One of them became a valiant warrior with whom the Sun Goddess was particularly well pleased, and on him she showered her divine favors.

This prince, Jimmu Tenno, was the first human emperor of Japan.

All subsequent emperors of Japan—for 2,600 years—have claimed descent from this grandson of the god Hoori and thus of the Sun Goddess. The descendants of the elder brother Hoderi, who promised submission after being engulfed in the waters induced by the Jewel of Flood Tide, are the Hayato—guards of the imperial palace. To this day a Japanese court dance represents the drowning struggles of Hoderi.

Hoori's building a special house in which the Sea Princess might bring forth her child reflects a custom persisting in Japan until comparatively recent times—that of having women bear their children in a room constructed just for this purpose apart from the main house. After the birth, the room was always burned.

In Japanese mythology the sea deities are dragons who have the power of assuming human shape. But at the moment of giving birth the Dragon Princess had to transform herself back into her native form, the dragon. Because the first human emperor, Jimmu Tenno, was a descendant of the Dragon Princess as well as of the Sun Goddess, the dragon is important in Japanese mythology and legend.

Japanese artists depict the Sea God—the Dragon King—as an aged, long-bearded man with a dragon coiled on his head or back. In his hand he carries the tide-ruling jewels. His messengers are shown with sea shells or scales clinging to their garments and usually with an octopus or a dragon on head or back.

When represented in its animal form the dragon is a huge reptile with a head like that of a camel and with a bright jewel under its whiskered chin. Some dragons have horns, others wings. They live in the oceans, lakes, or seas, though they can ascend to heaven at will. Their breath changes into clouds from which come either fire or rain.

The Dragon King is wise and noble, though he causes storms at sea when angered. In October, when all the gods assemble to arrange marriages, the Dragon King and his attendants rise from the waves. Heavens and ocean become radiant. The priest of the shrine goes to the beach and receives offerings from these denizens of the sea.

the grand imperial shrine

For three generations the descendants of the Sun Goddess had lived in the southernmost island, Kyûshû, where Ninigi had first descended to earth. But when Jimmu, grandson of Hoori and the Dragon Princess, rose to power as the first emperor of the land, he made a promise to Amaterasu: "I shall foster righteousness and extend the imperial rule so that in time the whole world will be under one roof."

After reigning for many years, Jimmu Tenno knew that he must begin to fulfill that promise. Summoning his brothers, sons, and brave generals he said: "Long ago when our ancestor Ninigi opened the sky barriers and came to earth, he brought divine wisdom from the Sun Goddess to a land wracked with violence. Many years have elapsed; disorders have again arisen, and there are still distant parts of the Central Land of Reed Plains that do not as yet enjoy the blessings of our imperial rule. Each hamlet has its own chief, and there is constant warfare among them. From the Lord of the Tide I have learned that far to the east lies a beautiful country surrounded by blue mountains. That is no doubt the center of the world. Let us go there to set up our capital that we may more easily rule over the land than from this distant spot."

Eagerly his listeners assented, and soon a long line of war vessels was edging northward along the eastern coast of Kyûshû. Upon reaching a narrow strip of water dividing their island from the larger one beyond, they hesitated, uncertain where to go.

Then an aged man seated on a turtle appeared before them. "Strike seaward!" he commanded. Humbly they obeyed, know-

ing well that the turtle was a messenger of the Sea God.

On they sailed, landing at point after point to battle against the native tribes and subject them to imperial rule. To aid Jimmu Tenno in his conquest of the country, the Sun Goddess opened the heavens and threw down a great sword and then sent an eight-legged crow to be his guide.

Greatly did the imperial forces need the help of the goddess, for in time they came to a place inhabited by hordes of savage and untamable people who lived like huge spiders in pits gouged from the earth. Fierce was the fighting against these ferocious creatures, but at length they bowed in defeat and Jimmu's warriors advanced in triumph.

Again and again the imperial forces were besieged by violent earth deities and chieftains. But the Sun Goddess continued to show her favor: into the skies she sent an immense golden fish hawk whose radiance so dazzled the eyes of the enemy that they were unable to fight.

On pressed the conquerors, exploring and fighting for seven years. Only once did they taste defeat. Forgetting in the excitement of battle the honors due their ancestress Amaterasu, one day they made an attack facing the sun. Swiftly the affronted goddess snatched the victory from them. Thereafter they fought with the sun at their backs only, and all was well.

Triumphant at last over the forces that tried to halt their progress through the land, they emerged from the northern end

of the Inland Sea and set up their capital in Yamato—the province
that for eight hundred years was to remain the seat of the imperial
power. A magnificent palace was erected in which Jimmu Tenno
could dwell in splendor. He established just laws to unify the
conquered provinces, and reigned wisely and long.

Emperor Jimmu and all his successors to the imperial throne
of Japan had three possessions that they prized above all others:
the sword taken by Susanoo from the eight-forked serpent, the
mirror that had enticed the Sun Goddess from the cave, and the
necklace of jewels. "Guard these treasures as emblems of your
divine power," Amaterasu had told the Heavenly Grandson
Ninigi before he descended to earth. "Revere especially the
mirror: look upon it as though it were I. Do this, and the prosperity of you and your descendants as divine rulers shall be as
everlasting as heaven and earth."

For many generations these sacred objects were kept in the
imperial palace on the couch of the emperor. Thus he was near
them night and day. The gifts were wrapped in costly silks that
they might never be soiled. When these coverings fell apart from
age, they were not removed but new silks were placed over them.
Thus the bundles became ever larger with the passing years.

But in time there came to the throne an emperor who could not
bear to have the holy emblems beside him at night. "Let a special
sanctuary be built," he decreed, "where the sacred sword, mirror,
and jewels may be kept safe and undefiled." Then he entrusted
the care of the three treasures to his daughter.

Unwilling at first, however, to be separated entirely from these
symbols of his divine power, he had replicas made for his couch.
But eventually he came to feel that even these were too holy to
be kept by his bedside, and special rooms were built for them in
the palace.

Then to the eleventh emperor of Japan came the command
of the Sun Goddess: "I am not pleased with the disposition of
the Sacred Treasures. Remove them to a more suitable place of
worship."

Calling his young daughter to his side, the emperor said, "To you I assign the most important of all tasks: find a spot worthy to become the final home of the divine gifts."

Throughout the land the princess journeyed until the Sun Goddess at last directed her footsteps to the province of Ise. Here on the banks of a river the maiden found a place where the rising sun smiled early and the setting sun lingered long. The hills were garlanded with silver streams and breezes rippled contentedly through luxuriant trees. Peace prevailed, for here the sound of roaring sea could not be heard.

64

In this tranquil haven a shrine was erected to house the Sacred Treasures, and soon worshippers from all parts of the land came to seek help and guidance and to pay homage to the glorious Goddess of the Sun.

The Grand Imperial Shrine of the Sun Goddess at Ise is the most sacred place in Japan. In its innermost sanctuary lies the sacred mirror, still wrapped in countless layers of white brocade. Upon coming to the throne, every emperor ceremoniously adds another covering.

To this shrine emperors throughout the centuries have reported national events to the goddess. It was here that Hirohito's messengers brought news of Japan's defeat in World War II.

Though the shrine dates back to the year 5 B.C., the buildings never become old. Every twenty years, on September 15, they are rebuilt in exactly the same way. Tiny charms are made from the wood of the former structure, the wearers thus having upon themselves a part of the former dwelling place of the Sun Goddess.

Duplicates of the Sacred Treasures are still kept in the imperial palace and are ceremoniously presented to each emperor upon his ascension to the throne. The mirror symbolizes knowledge; the sword, power; the jewels, mercy.

February 11, the date that Jimmu became emperor, is celebrated as a national holiday. One issue of bank notes depicts him receiving the divine cross-sword from the Sun Goddess.

prince yamato-take

At the shrine of the Sun Goddess at Ise knelt a young prince, praying that the deity would bring success to his venture. His father, the Emperor Keiko, had commanded the sixteen-year-old youth to travel down to the island of Kyûshû to subdue some rebellious tribes who were causing discontent and turmoil.

He looked up into the face of his aunt, high priestess of the shrine. In her hand she held a rich silk robe. "Take it," she said, "for good luck."

Into the western country the young prince and his followers journeyed. But as they reached the stronghold of the rebel leaders, they realized that they must resort to strategy. "I will go on alone," said the prince, "but in disguise." He dressed himself in the robe, let down his hair, placed an ornamented comb in it, and adorned himself with jewels. The handsome youth made a handsome woman.

Forcing himself to walk with tiny steps and assuming a shy, feminine manner, he slipped through the woods and into the tent where at that very moment the two enemy chieftains were discussing the rumor that a prince was on his way to enforce the rule of the emperor. Scornfully they laughed at the idea that anyone could subdue them: were they not the bravest, strongest fighters in the land?

They were delighted to see the beautiful girl who had come so unexpectedly out of the night. How refreshing to have their dinner served by one so fair! Again and again they lifted their cups just to have the pleasure of seeing her pour wine for them. Never had they known a more charming maiden.

But suddenly the maiden flung aside the silk robe and stood revealed as an armed warrior! His sword flashed, and one brigand fell dead at his feet. The other tried to plunge from the room but was caught and held by the agile prince. Admiration welled into the heart of the rebel chieftain. "Before you slay me," he gasped, "tell me who you are."

"I am the son of the Heavenly Sovereign of the Eight Great Islands," replied the prince.

"I thought my brother and I were the bravest and most clever of all men, but I was wrong," said the chieftain. "You should be called 'Yamato-Take, Japan Champion,' for you are the most courageous and cunning man in the land."

With their leaders gone, the rebellious tribes cowered before the brave prince. What his sword alone could not do, he accomplished by trickery. At length he returned in triumph to his father.

But Yamato-Take, for he had accepted the name given him by the brigands, was not allowed to remain home and enjoy his honors very long. Soon he was commanded to extend the power of the empire by quelling an uprising of the Ainu people in the eastern provinces. Once more he journeyed to Ise to pray at the shrine of the Sun Goddess. He would need her protection more than ever, for the Ainu were a fierce people.

Realizing his danger, the high priestess gave him one of the most precious possessions of the shrine—the sword taken so long ago by Susanoo from the tail of the eight-forked serpent. How could he fail with this divine treasure in his hand!

But he nearly did, for now it was his turn to be tricked. As he traveled into the distant provinces, he was greeted hospitably by one of the rulers. Banquets were spread before him, and a hunt was organized as part of the entertainment in his honor. Unsuspectingly Yamato pursued a deer into a wild plain covered with tall grass. Then all at once he became aware that he was alone and that fire surrounded him in every direction. There was no escape through those flaming walls. He was trapped! What strategy could save him now?

Then his hand tightened about the sword given him by the priestess. Here was divine aid! Sweeping the keen-edged weapon around in wide arcs, he swiftly cut down the grasses on all sides until he had cleared an area that offered no food for the hungry flames. Into futile nothingness they sputtered and hissed long before their scorching fingers could reach the youth.

Yamato-Take was saved, but there was no safety for his enemies. Like snowflakes in a torrential storm they scattered before the gleaming sword of the prince. When at length he left the province, its inhabitants had been subdued to the will of the emperor.

Now during the many years that Prince Yamato-Take was fighting throughout the land, he had been accompanied by his faithful wife Tachibana. Without complaint she had endured every hardship. But now her once-lovely face was burned by sun and roughened by wind, and the tiny hands were blistered. But the deepest wounds of all were in her heart. Often she kept her eyes averted from her husband that he might not see her tears, for she knew that he had fallen in love with the enchanting Princess Miyadzu whom he had met during their travels.

"I will come back and make you my bride," Tachibana had heard him whisper as they said farewell. He had looked up to see the sad face of his wife, but his eyes had hardened and she knew that he would keep his vow to return to the princess.

Yamato-Take's triumph had made him vain and haughty as well as unkind. One day as he reached the Straits of Kadzusa and the men were preparing boats for launching, he said impatiently, "This is a mere stream! I could leap across it if I were alone!" The god of the straits heard that foolish boast and was offended. Lashing winds and waves to screaming fury, he caused Yamato-Take's boat to toss and lurch so violently that the outraged timbers began to break.

Then Tachibana looked down into the frothing waters. "Forgive my husband's haughty words and let him live. Take my life in place of his!" Into the sea she leaped. Instantly the waves became peaceful billows, and the winds subsided into fragrant breezes. The god had accepted Tachibana's sacrifice: Yamato-Take was safe.

The prince went on to further conquests for the emperor, and his fame spread throughout the realm. But he never forgot the unselfish devotion of his wife. Many years passed. Then one day he returned and ascended a hill overlooking the spot where she had leaped into the sea. In remorse he cried, "Azuma wa ya!" which means "Ah, my wife!" From that time on, the eastern coast provinces in the area where Tachibana made her sacrifice were called "Azuma."

When Yamato-Take died, his soul in the form of a white bird soared from his burial mound, leaving only the hero's clothes in the tomb. Then it turned heavenward and was never seen again.

Yamato-Take, who lived in the second century, was one of Japan's most famous heroes. The Ainu whom he was sent to conquer were the original inhabitants of the country. For over a thousand years the Japanese warred against them until now their descendants live only in the northernmost island of the archipelago and on government-controlled reservations much like those of our American Indians.

Since the time of Yamato-Take the sacred sword has been called "Kusanagi," which means "grass cleaver." The exact spot where the hero fought the flames with the aid of the divine weapon is called "The Burnt Moor."

JINGO'S CONQUEST OF KOREA

To the Empress Jingo came a strange dream. A spirit seemed to say to her, "Across the sea to the west there is the luxuriant land of Korea, rich in treasure and fair as a beautiful woman. It is yours, O Empress, if you will but conquer it."

Hastening to her husband, who was playing upon his lute, she told him of her dream. "There is no such land to the west," he scoffed. "False, lying deities have deceived you. Think no more about this."

Then a voice came from the angry gods who had sent the dream. "No longer shall you be emperor of this empire! Step now into the inevitable path!"

The fingers slipped from the lute and the sweet tones died away. The emperor was dead.

Now the empress was ruler, and again her thoughts turned to the dream. Why should not she, even though a woman, invade Korea? To the gods she prayed, "If I am to undertake this quest, send me an omen! Let my hair be parted as I bathe!" She bathed, and the hair parted. Then she fished with three grains of rice as bait. Her catch was good: another lucky omen. Now she hesitated no longer. She would invade Korea!

Only with the help of the gods, however, could she succeed in so bold an undertaking. From the Deity of the Mountain she secured timber and iron with which to build ships; from the Deity of Grass, hemp for rope; from the Deity of Fields, rice for her army.

One thing more was needed. To the god of the shore the Empress Jingo said, "Go to your master, the Dragon King of the Sea. Bid him give me the Tide Jewels to insure my success." Isora disappeared into the waves and soon returned bearing the precious jewels that control the ebb and flow of the sea.

The three thousand ships of the empress were launched on tranquil waters. But lurking behind silver clouds was an avalanche of wind and rain that soon began to hammer so mercilessly on the vessels that their timbers shrieked in dismay.

In his undersea palace the Dragon King heard the howling tempest. "To the rescue of the Empress Jingo!" he shouted to his legion. From all corners of the sea they came and at a signal from the Dragon King went into action. Harried, despairing, the Japanese suddenly saw these monsters of the deep rising about them on every side. Flashing dragons grasped the ships' cables in their jaws and pulled them through sullen waters. Broad-backed creatures dived under floundering ships and lifted them aloft. Mammoth heads pushed reeling vessels smoothly over the billows. Not until the sea was calm did the monsters slip away into its depths.

On sailed the Japanese armada until the shores of Korea loomed on the horizon. As the fleet drew near, the empress saw that a mighty army, bristling with weapons, was waiting on the water's edge. Before them were ships manned and ready for launching. Sentinels at high places along the beach were alert and still, waiting for the word of command. It came, and now the Koreans flung themselves into their war vessels and sped toward the invaders. Bow strings taut, eyes fierce with determination, they bore down upon the Japanese fleet.

The empress waited until the ships were just beyond arrow range. Then she tossed the Jewel of the Ebb Tide into the sea. Instantly the waters receded as if sucked in by some cavernous mouth. Lower and lower they sank until the Korean ships came to a stop, stranded on moist sand. In consternation the Koreans stared at each other. "It is but a tidal wave," shouted their commander. "On by foot! Death to the invaders of our land!"

Out of the ships they swarmed, brandishing their weapons and sweeping over the sands to the enemy. Then the empress took the Jewel of the Flood Tide from the shell and flung it into the sea. Like a wild beast that has found its prey, the waters closed in about the terrified Koreans. They turned to flee, but there was no escape. Floundering helplessly, warrior after warrior was sucked into the greedy waves.

With their army destroyed, the Koreans could offer no further resistance. Triumphantly the empress entered the country and forced the king to pay homage. "My allegiance to you will last," he said, "until the sun rises in the west and sets in the east, until mountain streams flow backwards, and pebbles from river beds ascend the heavens to become stars." Then the defeated monarch gave the conquerors jewels, books, pictures, tiger skins, and precious robes—treasures to enrich the imperial household for generations. Smiths, weavers, and other artisans to instruct the Japanese in numerous useful arts were also in the ships that returned to the Land of the Dragonfly.

72

The Tide Jewels were caught by Isora and taken back to the Dragon King until mortals should again request their use to control the ocean waters.

According to the ancient books, the Empress Jingo—Japan's greatest heroine—subjugated Korea in the third century A.D. In art she is shown in the attire of a warrior and is often depicted writing the words "ruler of a state" on a rock with the tip of her bow.

It is customary in Japan to deify great heroes. This distinction came to Jingo, and a shrine was erected in her honor. Her son Hachiman was deified as the God of War. Through the centuries boys have prayed to them for strength and courage.

Part of the tribute given by defeated Korea was the Chinese classic, the Confucian *Analects*—a book that was to have a tremendous impact on Japanese thought and culture. Korea had very early been influenced by Chinese ideas; Japan borrowed from Korea what Korea had borrowed from China. But Japan always made her borrowings distinctly her own.

Greek mythology also has a woman warrior, the Amazon Queen Penthesilea (penth ah sill ee' ah) who fought against the mighty Achilles before the walls of Troy.

the land of the dragonfly

The Japanese have a phrase, "the Ah-ness of things," that expresses their sense of wonder and delight at the beauty of nature. The poets describe red azaleas as being the fires of the gods, and the snow on Mount Fuji as the robes of heavenly beings. Happy parties go out to rejoice in the majesty of flaming maple leaves in autumn or to witness the delicate panoply of cherry blossoms in spring. Gardens are diminutive landscapes graced with picturesque stone lanterns, tiny arched bridges, waterfalls, and camellia-bordered pools. One emperor is said to have covered the miniature mountains in his garden with white silk in mid-summer to simulate snow.

Within such settings as these, it is not surprising that Japanese legend includes many charming stories of moon maidens who come to earth in robes of feathers, or of lonely star lovers separated by the Milky Way.

But all is not delicate and lovely in Japanese legend. There are also tales of three-eyed Oni and of malicious Kappa who can be overcome only if the water is spilled from a hollow cup which they have in their skulls. Ghost stories and tales of animals with supernatural power also abound. The ghosts are frequently women and can be detected because they have no feet. And one must be wary about a beautiful lady who is a stranger, for she may turn out to be a fox that has transformed itself into human shape to trick people. Then there are grateful animals and insects like the bee that rewarded kindness by helping to win a battle.

The heroes of Japanese legend are a dauntless group who conquer a choice array of monsters such as a centipede that wraps itself three times around a mountain, and a severed head that dangles in mid-air, spouting fire.

Japanese legends, which like the myths are interwoven with religious beliefs, often show a fascinating intermingling of Shinto

74

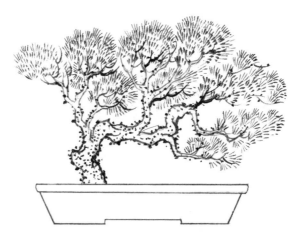

and Buddhist ideas. When priests first brought Buddhism to Japan in the Sixth Century, many people feared that the native deities would be offended. But it is said that the emperor consulted the Sun Goddess at Ise and was told in a dream that she would welcome the erection of Buddhist temples. Buddhist teachers taught that all Shinto gods were actually just forms of Buddhist deities. Shintoists reversed the order and said that the native deities were the originals, the Buddhist gods being merely representations of them. Thus the two religions overlapped and existed together. Nowadays a "god shelf" for Shinto deities and an altar for Buddha are found in almost all homes. This duality of religion multiplies the number of deities tremendously, of course, especially since every malady is controlled by both Shinto and Buddhist gods. To cure warts, for example, one must petition two Buddhist and two Shinto deities.

The Japanese love tiny things. Sometimes they make exquisite gardens, complete in every detail, on spaces no larger than a dinner tray. They cherish their dwarf trees, some only one or two feet high though they may be over a hundred years old. But nowhere is this delight both in the miniature and in nature more evident than in their poetry. Centuries ago they discovered that they could express even their most poignant feelings in tiny, thirty-one-syllable poems called "tanka." Susanoo's song about the clouds may possibly be the very oldest of these poems in literature. The tanka consists of only five lines and has neither rhyme nor rhythm. The first line has five syllables; the second line, seven; the third line, five; the fourth line, seven; the fifth line, seven. Every year the emperor sponsors a world-wide tanka contest, awarding prizes for the best entries during the New Year cele-bration. In recent years prizes have on several occasions been won by California poets. Here is a tanka:

The rippling sea-swell	(5 syllables)
Curling upon the gold sand,	(7 syllables)
And, curving over,	(5 syllables)
A bough of cherry blossoms—	(7 syllables)
Youth shielding eternal age.	(7 syllables)

The "haiku," which developed about a thousand years later than tanka, is still shorter, consisting of but three lines and having only seventeen syllables.

Ah, cunning firefly!	(5 syllables)
Just beyond our finger tips	(7 syllables)
Hiding in moonlight.	(5 syllables)

76

Almost all Japanese, from emperor to gardener, write these tiny poems. Fifty monthly magazines are devoted solely to haiku, and daily newspapers have sections for them. Over a million are published annually. It has been said that the Japanese write poetry because they live poetry. Even their national anthem is poetic: "May our Lord's Empire live through a thousand years till tiny pebbles grow into giant boulders covered with emerald mosses." The ancient Greeks had a muse, or goddess, who inspired a few talented individuals to poetic heights. Not so with the Japanese: poetry belongs to all of them. A Japanese author once said, "What man does not write poetry on hearing the song of the nightingale among the flowers?"

Themes of haiku are what one would expect of people to whom all nature is infused with divine spirit: the little poems are about fireflies, flowers, the seasons, snow. But haiku are far more than delicate word-pictures: they may express the deepest feelings of the human heart, as does this one written by the famous poet Chiyo after the death of her small son:

> How far has he gone,
> My hunter of dragonflies,
> What does he hunt now?

Japanese legend and art often picture the souls of children playing in a celestial garden with flowers and butterflies just as they did on earth. Perhaps the mother is wistfully hoping that Jizo, the kind god who cares for the souls of children and wraps them up in his long sleeves when they are lonely, will be especially watchful over her little boy. A good haiku, like all real poetry, suggests far more than it actually says.

Japan's classical No drama is heavily indebted to myth and legend, almost all its themes coming from these ancient stories. The earliest No dramas were really religious observances, acted only at shrines. The word "No" means "talent" or "accomplishment," and the plays are combinations of poetry, music, dance, and pantomime. They are performed only by men, who take feminine as well as masculine roles. As in Greek drama, the main characters wear masks and there is a chorus. These plays, like the tanka and haiku, are very short, lasting usually less than an hour though several may be presented together to make an evening's entertainment.

Yes, the Japanese like tiny things. Perhaps that is why in the legend "Buddha and the Whale" they seem to be poking a bit of fun—but gently—at the gigantic bronze statue of Buddha in the city of Kamakura. The whale challenges the statue...

The beautiful, grotesque, ghostly, heroic, and humorous: Japanese legends are among the very best in the world.

the ROBe OF feathers

78 One day a fisher lad named Hairukoo was strolling along a
wooded shore, reveling in the glories of the spingtime. Suddenly
he stopped short in amazement. On a pine tree before him hung
an exquisite robe of pure white feathers—a robe so delicate in
workmanship and texture that moonbeams seemed to have been
woven into its glossy folds.

As he took it down, he heard a frightened little gasp behind
him. He turned to see a maiden emerging from the sea, her hands
held imploringly toward him. "The robe is mine, kind sir," she
cried. "May I have it now?"

The maiden, like the robe, was entrancingly beautiful, and for
a few moments the lad could do nothing but gaze in speechless
wonder. Then he clasped the garment more closely. He, a poor
fisher lad, could never hope to win so fair a maiden as this for a
bride, but he could keep her robe to remind him always of this
moment when the radiance of stars, moon, and sun all in one
seemed to have taken feminine form before him.

"No," he replied, "I found the robe and shall keep and treasure
it always."

The maiden's eyes filled with tears. "But without it I cannot
soar into the heavens and return to my celestial home in the moon!
I beg of you, give it back to me!" she pleaded.

A being from the shimmering heavens! Now Hairukoo was
more determined than ever to keep the robe. But as her eyes
darkened in despair, he relented.

"I will return your robe of feathers," he said, "if you will dance for me. Often have I heard of the grace of the moon maidens; fill my heart and eyes with a vision of loveliness that I can cherish always."

Joyfully she replied, "I will dance as my sisters and I do in the great banquet hall of the Moon Palace. But first I must have my robe of feathers. Without it I can do nothing at all."

"No," said the fisher boy, suddenly suspicious. "If I give it back, you will fly away without dancing for me."

For an instant an angry shadow dimmed the beauty of the maiden's face. "Mortals break their promises," she said reproachfully, "but the Heavenly Beings, never!"

Without another word he handed her the robe. She put it over her shoulders, drew a tiny musical instrument from its folds, and began to sing and dance. Her song told of the strange and faraway kingdom of the moon where thirty celestial princes resided— fifteen robed in silver when the moon was full, fifteen in lustrous black when it was waning. For a few magic moments Hairukoo felt as if he, a poor fisher lad, were a part of that resplendent throng.

Then the maiden, singing a song of love for Japan, wrapped her robe of feathers more closely around her and rose into the air. Above the pines and mountain summits she soared until she was enfolded in the silvery wreaths of the moon.

The Japanese show great love for this story, having written hundreds of poems about it and made it the subject of one of their most famous No dramas.

A remnant of the robe of feathers is believed to be preserved in a shrine at Cape Miho in Suruga Province, and a nearby tree is said to be the very one on which the lad found it.

the star lovers

The maiden Tanabata was very happy in her celestial cloud-palace weaving garments for her father, God of the Firmament, until the day that she chanced to see the handsome young cowherd Hikoboshi. Then she found her eyes straying often from the loom to watch him tend his oxen on the Plain of High Heaven. And Hikoboshi, once having caught sight of the maiden, discovered that the very best grass for his oxen seemed to grow in the meadows just below the cloud-palace.

Tanabata's father, reading their hearts and eyes, knew they were in love and consented to their marriage. Then the maid and youth were wondrously happy as they roamed the Plain of High Heaven hand in hand, wanting only to be together always.

For a while the father watched them indulgently, delighting in their joy. But gradually he became annoyed. Tanabata was no longer weaving the silken garments, and Hikoboshi was allowing his oxen to wander about untended. They found time for nothing but each other.

At last the God of the Firmament became angry and decided that if their love made them neglect their work, they must be denied that love. "Henceforth you will be separated by the Tranquil River of Heaven," he decreed. "Only once a year, on the seventh day of the seventh month, may you see each other."

The maid and youth parted, she going back to her weaving and he to tending his oxen. But the joy that had flamed in their hearts now lay like cold ashes in a spent fire.

The lonely months finally spun themselves into the past, and the time for their meeting drew near. Anxiously they watched the stars and clouds. What if rains were to swell the river beyond its banks and make it impossible for them to cross! Then their reunion would be postponed for another year! But on the seventh day of the seventh month the Plain of High Heaven was suffused in gossamer mists of lavender and gold as the lovers hastened toward the river from opposite directions.

At the water's edge they paused in dismay. How were they to cross that vast expanse! Then the air was filled with the rustle of wings as a great flock of magpies descended to the Tranquil River of Heaven. Over its shining surface they hovered, wings out-spread, to make a bridge for the lovers so that not a moment of their precious day together would be lost. Tanabata and Hiko-boshi sped across the feathered passageway into each other's arms, and around them twinkled a cloudburst of rainbow-colored stars.

Through the ages the weaver and her cowherd have patiently borne the loneliness of twelve long months by clinging to a dream that becomes glorious reality when at last they meet for their one beautiful day together. And the faithful magpies have continued down the long reaches of time to perform their own gentle service of love.

Japan is a land of joyous festivals that, because there is no weekly day of rest like our Sundays, are the real holidays. One of the most popular and romantic of them all celebrates the yearly reunion of the star lovers and is known as the Festival of Tanabata. Freshly cut bamboo placed on roofs or in gardens is decorated with bright strips of paper—blue, red, green, yellow, white—to symbolize the stars that glow with color for this happy occasion. Each strip of paper bears a tiny love poem, either tanka or haiku. Children sing "O Weather, be fair!" for if it rains the feathers of the birds may be too damp and heavy to span the river, the Milky Way.

Tanabata and Hikoboshi represent two stars, Vega and Altair, which are on opposite sides of the Milky Way. Their legend is very ancient, many poems about it being in Japan's oldest and most famous collection of poetry, the *Manyoshu*, which dates back to the Eighth Century.

The magpie is a symbol of love-making.

willow wife

All the villagers loved the great willow tree. In summer they
delighted in the cool lacy patterns its sun-drenched branches
drew on the ground. In winter they were fascinated by the picturesque little towers and temples etched by the snow on every
leaf and twig.

But the youth Heitaro cherished the tree most of all. Each
morning and night as he went to and from his fields, he paused
to luxuriate in its serene loveliness. On moonlit evenings his joy
in it surged even more warmly through his heart as he sat beneath the whispering branches.

One day Heitaro was dismayed to hear that the villagers were
planning to build a bridge over the river and wanted to use the
willow tree for timber. "It has served us for a long time as a tree,"
they said; "now let it serve us as a bridge."

His beautiful tree to be trampled upon all day by busy feet!
How could he endure this indignity to his beloved willow! What
could ever take its place! Hastening to the elders of the village, he
pleaded, "Let the willow stand! Gladly will I give you all the
wood you need from my own trees. Behind my house are many
that will make good timber for a bridge, but there can never be
another like our willow!" To his infinite relief, Heitaro saw the
elders nod their heads, and the stately tree continued to stand.

Many years passed. Then one night when Heitaro strolled
toward the willow, he saw a young girl, fair as the tree itself,
standing in its tremulous shadows. As she seemed to be waiting

for someone, the youth bowed and began to withdraw. "I will go home," he said kindly, "so that you may be alone with him whom you seek."

Smiling, she answered, "He is already here. He is always here." Then she slipped away into the night.

All the next day Heitaro found himself thinking about the maiden, and he looked forward even more eagerly than usual to visiting the willow. There, in the cool of the evening, he found her again. This time they talked of many things, but mostly about the great willow. By the third night he knew that he had fallen in love with this gentle maid whose soul seemed to have as deep a communion with the tree as did his own.

"Be my wife," he said, "for should not we who both love the willow love each other?"

"Yes," she whispered, "but first I must implore you not to ask questions about me or where I came from. Some day you will understand."

"It shall be as you ask," he promised.

Heitaro and the maiden were married. With every passing day, month, and year the glow of love deepened in her eyes, and the peace Heitaro had always found in the tree now seemed to fill every corner of his modest house.

Then came the proclamation. The emperor wished to build a temple to Kwannon, Goddess of Mercy. Throughout the land came messengers inviting each village to contribute the best timber for the sacred building. "We must give our willow," said the elders. "What greater tribute could we pay to the beloved Kwannon?"

Again Heitaro pleaded for his cherished willow. But this time his entreaties went unheeded, for none of the trees that he offered in its stead were deemed worthy to grace the temple of a goddess.

Sorrowfully he told his wife, "They are going to take our tree. Once I could not have endured its loss, but your love has brought a joy into my life that can heal every wound, even this one."

She turned to him in anguish and then crumpled into his arms like a broken flower. "My willow wife, my willow wife," he cried as he sought to comfort her. "Would that I could save the tree for you whom I love so dearly."

That night his slumber was shattered by a scream of terror. "It has begun!" his wife sobbed. "They are cutting down the tree in the moonlight! They slash and tear at my body; my hair is being trampled under their heavy feet! Fiercer and fiercer are the blows! For I am the soul of the willow tree, Heitaro, and when it falls I too must go. Farewell!"

A thunderous crash drowned out the sound of her cries. Heitaro sprang to the door. There in the moonlight lay the great tree, its branches still quivering as if wracked with pain. He wheeled back into the room in terror to find his loved one.

Willow Wife had disappeared.

To the nature-loving Japanese, trees and flowers have a special symbolism and significance. They are often regarded as having souls not unlike those of people and thus can love, suffer, and feel joy.

The pine tree is frequently planted at the garden gate to bring good luck, and the double-trunked camellia symbolizes a happy married life. The leaves of the willow, together with the blossoms of the cherry and other trees, make up the delicate brocade woven by the Deity of Springtime.

urashima

86   The fisher lad Urashima caught a tortoise on his line one day.
A pity to harm it, he thought, for these creatures are said to live
a thousand years. He allowed it to slip back into the sea, and
again baited his hook for a fish. But the day was warm, and the
youth soon fell fast asleep as his boat drifted idly on the quiet
waters.

"Urashima, Urashima!" Through his dreams came the sound
of his name being called again and again. He awoke to find the
tortoise by his boat. "You were kind to me," it said. "Let me repay
by taking you down to the Palace of the Dragon King where the
Sea Princess herself may thank you."

Here was adventure! Eagerly Urashima climbed on the creature's broad back and down they glided through the sea lanes
into the shining depths.

It was not long before he could see the delicate tracery of
towers, pillars, and bridges spiraling up through the emerald
waters. Then it seemed as if the rainbow had fallen into the sea,
for a magnificent procession of fish—silver, green, gold, red—
formed on either side to escort them to the Dragon King's palace.

When the pearled gates swung open, the lad drew back in awe.
Before him was a land of enchantment. Here all the four seasons
presented their glories at once: spring with its blossoming cherry
and silken-winged butterflies; summer's gardenias bending over
shimmering pools; autumn's blaze of maple leaves; winter's white
embroidery on tree and fern.

But the beauty of the Sea Princess who came forward to greet him eclipsed all of these wonders, and when she spoke it was as if every singing bird had given her its sweetest note. "You were kind to my messenger, the tortoise," she said. "Stay with us as long as you wish in this land of eternal youth that we may show our gratitude." She clapped her hands, and a great company of fishes glided in bearing on their fins coral trays heaped with delicacies. While the princess and Urashima feasted, other merry little fishes entertained them with song and dance.

For three years he stayed in the Palace of the Dragon King, finding new delights with every hour. But then he began to worry about his aged parents. How they must be grieving at his strange disappearance!

"Let me return for one day to my home," he said to the Sea Princess. "Then I will come back to dwell forever in this beautiful realm."

"I had hoped to make you so happy that you would never leave," she answered sadly, for she had fallen in love with the gentle lad from the great world above the waters. "But if you must go, take this gift." She handed him a small box. "It contains a valuable treasure—one that should not be seen by mortal eyes. Take it as a token of my love, but I entreat you, do not open it!"

Urashima promised, and mounting the tortoise, was swiftly borne upward to earth. But as he stepped upon the beach, he found to his amazement that everything had changed. Where was the old tree under which he had dozed so often? Where was his father's house? The stream ran through the village as always, but now it was spanned by a new bridge that he had never seen before.

Bewildered, he stopped an old woman and asked, "Where is Urashima's home? What has become of his parents?"

She stared at him suspiciously. "Urashima? I have lived here eighty years and never have I heard of Urashima." She started to hobble away and then turned back. "Wait! Vaguely I remember hearing my old grandmother tell about a fisher lad by that name who was drowned at sea. But that was three hundred years ago!"

Tears welled into Urashima's eyes. How could he have forgotten that in the country of the Sea King one day was like a hundred years! Now everyone he loved on earth was gone! He would go back at once to his dear princess in the place where the four seasons displayed their glories at once, and where fishes danced on their tails and played musical instruments with their fins.

But where was the tortoise? How could he return? What if he were never to see his princess again! The box! Surely in the box he could discover the secret of returning to the sea. Perhaps she had given it to him for that very reason.

With trembling fingers he lifted the lid. A wreath of white smoke coiled out, wove itself into a delicate column above his head for a moment, and then drifted out over the sea. Now Urashima felt a change come over him. His limbs suddenly felt stiff and tired; his eyes became so dim that shore and sea faded away into a vague mist; the wind caught at a long white beard that fell to his waist.

"The princess had sealed my youth in the box, and I have let it go!" He staggered forward, lifted his arms imploringly to the sea, and then fell upon the sands. Urashima was dead.

The tale of Urashima, of which there are numerous variants, is one of the oldest and most loved in Japanese literature. It appears in the ancient records and also as a ballad, "The Fisher Boy," in the famous old anthology of Japanese poetry, the *Manyoshu*.

Urashima's fishing line and the box that contained his youth are still preserved at one of the temples near Yokohama.

Japanese artists show Urashima as an old man on the back of a tortoise or with an opened box in his hand.

Be cautious about boxes. When Urashima opened his, he brought trouble upon himself. When Pandora of Greek mythology opened hers, she brought trouble upon the whole world.

ISSUNBOSHI

"Send us a son, even if he be no longer than one of our fingers!"

Thus prayed the old man and old woman at the shrine of the deified Empress Jingo. When they rose to go, they seemed to hear a voice whisper from behind the shrine's bamboo curtain: "Your prayers will be granted."

But when their son was born, they were a bit disappointed, for he really was no bigger than a little finger. Their prayers needn't have been taken quite so literally! "We'll name him Issunboshi, One-Inch-Boy," grumbled the old woman, "but I do hope he grows up to be as big as other children."

But Issunboshi didn't. At the age of thirteen he was still as tiny as on the day he was born, and the neighbors called him all kinds of nicknames such as "Little Finger" and "Grain of Corn." Despite his size, however, Issunboshi was a brave fellow and stoutly stood up for his rights among the other boys.

Noticing, though, that his parents were ashamed of his wee stature, he decided to go out into the world alone. "Just give me a needle, a soup bowl, and chopsticks," he told them, "and I can get along very well."

He buckled on the needle as a sword, used the bowl and chopsticks as boat and oars, and sailed down the river to the capital city of Kyoto. Straight to the gates of the palace he went.

"A request! A request!" he called, cupping his tiny hands around his mouth to make the sound carry. Quite by accident the prince heard that faraway little voice but had to look around a long while before discovering to whom it belonged. Picking up the lad in his hand, the prince inquired what boon he wanted. "To live in the palace with you as your servant," was the prompt reply.

Now Issunboshi hardly seemed adequate for any of the ordinary jobs of the household, but what a charming page he would make for the young Princess Sanjo! "I will put my daughter in your care," said the prince gravely. "Don't let anything happen to her!"

Issunboshi was delighted with his assignment. Flourishing his needle and setting his cap at a jaunty angle, he vowed that the protection of Princess Sanjo had at that moment became the beginning, the middle, and the end of his existence.

Shortly afterward the page escorted his mistress to the temple of the Goddess Kwannon. As they were returning, two Oni leaped from behind the trees and stood in their path, leering maliciously. The princess screamed in fright. She had seen Oni before, of course—these pesky creatures were everlastingly trooping up from the underworld to cause trouble—but one never gets

used to Oni. These two were especially ugly. One was bright
pink, the other blue. Neither wore any clothing except a loin
cloth of tiger skin. Their mouths were nasty gashes extending
clear across their faces and pointing up at the corners toward
sharp horns. One of them even had an extra eye bulging from the
middle of his forehead, though his feet and hands had only three
toes and three fingers each.

Issunboshi climbed down from the shoulder of the princess and
planted himself squarely in front of the pink Oni. Waving his
sword he shouted, "Make way! Make way for the Princess Sanjo!"

The Oni hooted. "Why, I could swallow you in one gulp," said the pink one. "In fact, I think I will!" With that he popped the little fellow into his mouth. Down the slippery cavern slid Issunboshi so fast that the wind flattened his ears. He jolted to a rude stop in the pit of a stomach whose walls and floor quivered like nervous jellyfish. It was extremely hot and disagreeable down here, and Issunboshi had no intention of staying. Out came his needle. This way and that he slashed at the stomach walls, until the Oni bellowed with pain and fell into a fit of coughing that sent Issunboshi spinning out into the sunny world again.

The tiny page, damp but unharmed, picked up his cap and once more stalked toward the Oni. "Make way for the princess!" he commanded again. Then the blue Oni said, "Big talk, little bamboo shoot! I'll soon stop your noise!" But he wasn't very bright, for he had no original ideas at all as to how to get rid of a finger-sized boy. He too popped Issunboshi into his mouth and tried to swallow him whole. But this time the lad caught at the sides of the Oni's throat with his needle-sword and checked his fall. Then, hacking footholds for himself, he scaled the sheer cliffs and climbed over the quivering mountain that bobbed up in his pathway. In no time at all he was scrambling through the Oni's nostril—a long and gloomy tunnel indeed—and was industriously stabbing the creature's three eyes with his needle.

The two demons had had enough. Off they ran, howling with pain—one holding his upset stomach and the other his sore throat. Issunboshi bowed low before his princess. "So sorry for the delay!"

"My brave, dear little page!" she cried. "My father will reward you handsomely for this. But look! The Oni have dropped something!"

She stooped and picked up a small wooden object. "Why, it is their magic mallet," she exclaimed. "Now we're in luck! One has only to tap the magic mallet of an Oni on the ground, make a wish, and it is always granted. What do you want more than anything else in the world, Issunboshi?"

"To be as big as other people," he replied promptly.

The princess tapped the mallet on the ground and made the wish. In a flash Issunboshi shot up to the size of other boys of his age.

Now he was famous. The prince rewarded him with a roomful of gifts, the emperor summoned him to court and made him a high official, and the people cheered whenever he came into the streets. The princess waited until he grew a bit more and then married him. "If a finger-sized Issunboshi can conquer two Oni singlehanded," she must have reasoned, "just imagine what a full-sized Issunboshi could do!"

94

As for him, he loved his princess devotedly forever and ever for having made a man of him.

The Oni are evil spirits of many sizes, shapes, and colors from huge black ogres to small green goblins. All are trouble makers. Sometimes they are terrible creatures, sometimes merely comic. But the Japanese usually think of Oni as ugly demons who come up from the underworld. Though they constantly meddle in human affairs, they can be easily deceived and outwitted just as they were in this story. Bamboo screens can be helpful in keeping them away, for Oni must travel in straight lines and therefore would never go around the corners to get into enclosures behind the screen. Many of them possess the magic mallet than can grant wishes.

Japanese boys and girls play a game similar to our "Puss in the Corner," except for them it is "Oni in the Corner."

Women must be careful never to become jealous or they just might be changed into Oni.

A gay nursery song, "Issunboshi" is very popular with Japanese children. Adults too like the wee fellow, for his story is often represented on the No stage.

When the Japanese clean their houses from top to bottom for the New Year—as they always do—they expel any Oni that might be lurking around by saying, "Devils out! Luck enter!"

the oni and the wen

One night a group of Oni were dancing and singing out in the
woods when one of them heard a distinctly human chuckle. They
stopped their music at once and shook their green fists. Who was
daring to spy on their merrymaking and, worse, to laugh! Darting
about in all directions through the grasses and trees, they found
a hollow log. Inside was a little old man all crouched up, trying
hard to make himself invisible or at least like a knot in the wood.
No use. In went their three-fingered hands and out came the
little old man.

They popped him into the middle of the clearing and demanded, "What are you doing here and why did you laugh?"

"I was s-s-saught in the corm, I mean caught in the s-storm,"
he stuttered, so frightened he couldn't talk straight, "and I crept
into the hollow log· for shelter. There I fell asleep and was
awakened by your music. I laughed because you frolic so gaily
that I was reminded of my own happy youth when I was the
best dancer in the village."

"You?" they whooped, looking at his crooked legs and knobby
knees. "Then show us! Give us some fun!"

The old man really had been an excellent dancer in his youth,
but now his limbs creaked and crackled, and his feet kept duck-
ing in at the ankles in the most dismal way. But gradually as the
Oni's music grew livelier, so did he. With every step he regained
some of his former skill and grace. Soon he was having so much
fun that he forgot all about the Oni.

They were delighted with his performance. "You must come back tomorrow night to dance for us," they said. "But we need some pledge to make sure you will return."

"We could take an ear," said one. "I prefer his nose," said another. A third eyed his left arm covetously.

As he listened to these disagreeable suggestions, the old man's brain became as nimble as his feet had been. For a long time he had been afflicted with a large lump on his left cheek. Every year it became bigger and uglier, and he had despaired of ever getting rid of it. Here was his chance!

Twisting his face into a woeful expression, he whimpered, "Oh sirs, please take an ear or nose, but I beg of you, do leave my wen! No one in the village has one so big and red as mine!"

"Take the wen! Then we know he'll come back to get it and to dance for us!" shouted the perverse creatures. And off it came.

The delighted old man hobbled home, caught his wife about the waist and capered around the room with her, babbling, "My wen is gone! My wen is gone! My ugly, ugly wen is gone!" The neighbors, hearing the commotion, hurried over to see what had happened, and soon everyone in the village was rejoicing with the ecstatic old man. That is, all except one grumpy fellow who was never happy with anyone's good fortune except his own. He too had a wen, and the one thought that squeezed itself into his mind was how he might get the Oni to take it off just as they had the old man's.

"Tell me where their rendezvous is," he said to his neighbor. "Tonight I shall entertain them."

"Certainly, certainly," was the reply. "One old man's cavorting is as good as another's." Then he gave exact instructions.

But the neighbor's dancing was as clumsy as his disposition was sour, and the Oni were disappointed and insulted. "You perform atrociously tonight," they grumbled. "Take your old pledge and go home!" Then they clapped the wen onto the old man's cheek and hustled him out of the forest.

And now he had two!

the GOBLIN of OyeyAMA

High on the peaks of Mount Oyeyama in Tamba Province lived the Goblin King Shutendoji, a terrifying Oni who could assume any shape he pleased. Into the valley he would sweep at night and carry off young girls and boys to his mountain stronghold to provide sport and feasting for himself and his evil horde. "Human blood is his only drink!" said the terrified people.

But when he dared to come into Kyoto and snatch away the emperor's daughter, the clamor for a hero to slay this monster resounded throughout the realm. "The warrior Raiko is the bravest of all men," came the cry. "Let him search out Shutendoji!"

Raiko consented. Gathering brave companions about him, he devised a plan to outwit the Oni, for human force alone could never prevail against such a creature. "We will go disguised as mountain priests, with our weapons concealed in knapsacks over our shoulders," he decided. "But first we must pray to the gods for help. Let us seek the protection of Hachiman, god of war, and Kwannon, goddess of mercy."

Their devotions to the deities completed, the brave band journeyed to the mountain. But as they gazed at its jagged cliffs and chasms, they recoiled in dismay. How could mortals hope to ascend those perilous heights!

Suddenly two old men stood before them. "Here is a magic drink, harmless to men but not to goblins," said one, giving Raiko a large vessel. "You will need it when you reach Shutendoji."

"And you *will* reach him," said the other, "for the gods are helping you." Then a cloud descended, wrapped the men in billowing coils, and wafted them away.

"The deities to whom we prayed for protection! They are with us! Now we cannot fail!" said Raiko.

With new hope the men began to fight their way into thorny underbrush that lay like a strangling collar at the base of the mountain. They slashed through forests, crawled up precipices, and plunged into rivers. On and up they toiled until they reached a high plateau. There by a stream they saw a young girl washing heaps of torn and bloody garments. "I am a captive of Shutendoji, waiting my turn to die," she told them, and her slender body shook as she related the horrors that came with each day in the Goblin King's stronghold.

"We are warriors in disguise," said Raiko grimly. "Take us to the Oni. Perhaps he shall find that men, with the help of the gods, are mightier than he!"

Into a black iron palace the girl led them, past guards who jeered at the mountain priests foolish enough to come to the dwelling of the Goblin King for shelter. Heavy doors swung open, and there in a vast hall was Shutendoji. Eight feet tall he stood. His bright red skin seemed almost to be on fire, and his gimlet eyes bored through shocks of tangled white hair.

"We are poor priests who seek your hospitality," said Raiko.

"Then sit down and feast with us," said the Oni, and his shoulders rocked with evil laughter as he contemplated the after-dinner entertainment he would provide for these simple priests. He clapped his three-fingered hands, and frightened young girls staggering under heavy trays of food hurried in. Raiko and his companions clenched their hands beneath their long sleeves. How many homes in Kyoto had been made desolate by the disappearance of these maidens!

When the feast was over, Raiko bowed before the Goblin King and handed him a cup of the magic drink given by the deities. "We have enjoyed your drink; now do us the honor of trying

ours." The Goblin King drained the cup. "Better than mine!" he said, glaring at his trembling servants for not having served him wine as good as this. "More!"

His noisy companions demanded their share also, and the cups were filled again and again. "Now entertain us!" roared Shuten-doji. Raiko and his men began to sing and dance for the odious crew, but managed to keep the wine flowing. When the whole goblin company had drooped over the banquet table in drunken sleep, Raiko and his retainers dressed themselves in armor. At that moment the two deities appeared. "We have bound the hands and feet of Shutendoji. You, Raiko, cut off his head while your men slay the other Oni."

The warrior unsheathed his sword and with one blow sliced through the Goblin King's neck. But the head did not fall! Like a hissing geyser it shot straight into the air, spewing flame and venomous smoke. In an instant Raiko was engulfed in a swirling torrent of fire. But he did not falter. Scorched and choked, he stood his ground and again thrust his sword into the grisly head that careened dizzily in mid-air above him. Even higher it leaped and hung suspended out of reach, still belching flame. Then it crashed down upon Raiko's helmet, and the warrior felt the crunch of fangs into metal. But the deities had not deserted him: a moment later the head tumbled to the floor and was still. The goblin of Oyeyama was no more.

Getting monsters drunk before dispatching them seems to have been a popular procedure among heroes of old. Odysseus used it in dealing with the one-eyed Polyphemus (polly fee′ muss) of Greek mythology just as effectively as did Susanoo against the eight-forked serpent and Raiko against the Goblin King.

watanabe and the oni

"Don't go near the Rashomon Gate! A frightful Oni lurks there night after night!"

When this rumor reached the ears of Watanabe, he went into action at once. Was he not a follower of the great Raiko? Had he not gone with his master to slay the Goblin King of Oyeyama? How then could he be afraid of anything?

Riding out to the Rashomon Gate one night, Watanabe wrote his name and a poem on a slip of paper, which he attached to a post to prove that he had been there. No, he wasn't afraid, but one never knows how an encounter with an Oni will turn out. Then he stationed himself in the shadows by the gate and waited. Hours passed, but nothing more exciting occurred than the squabbles of a monkey colony in the nearby woods.

It was the kind of balmy night that stirs the cicadas to their best musical efforts, and Watanabe had almost been lulled to sleep by their rhythmic chirping when suddenly he felt a sharp tug at his helmet. Collecting his foggy wits, he leaped back and slashed at a black, indistinguishable shape crouched at the top of the gate. His sword cut through something, and a piercing shriek split the air. Cicadas and monkeys froze to silence and then came the thud of an object dropping to the ground. Watanabe picked it up, but nearly dropped it again: it was the huge, freshly severed arm of an Oni!

He raced home and jammed the ugly limb into a great stone chest. Never would he show it to anyone. Then for seven days he stayed in his house, seeing neither friend nor family while undergoing a rigid ritual of purification to rid himself of the evil creature's contamination.

On the seventh day an old woman knocked at his door. He peered at her through a crack and said, "Go away. I cannot have visitors yet."

"Visitor!" she said. "I am not a visitor; I am your old nurse! For years I have wanted to see the black-eyed baby I used to hold in my arms. Come now, let me in, for I have only a few moments to spare."

Watanabe hesitated, and then opened the door. She hobbled in and made herself comfortable. Her bright eyes darted about the room. "Ah, I see that you have acquired many fine things since leaving your father's house. Whatever is in that big stone chest?"

"That I cannot tell," said Watanabe.

"Can't tell! To your old nurse? You used to tell me everything!" she sniffed. "Come, come, let me peek in the chest!"

Watanabe was a bit uneasy; he really wasn't being very polite to this bent little old woman who had helped him learn to walk and picked him up when he stumbled.

"Just one look!" she wheedled.

"A quick one then!"

He opened the chest. With a whoop of delight the old woman pounced upon the arm and hugged it to her bosom. Then before Watanabe's goggling eyes she changed into a horned Oni and flew out of the house. As she sped down the road he heard her chortle, "My precious arm, my precious arm, I shall never lose you again!"

This story has been used by many Japanese artists. Frequently just the arm is shown, but some pictures depict a small, tearful Oni squatting on an immense arm, presumably bewailing the bad luck of the larger Oni who lost it. In still other cases Watanabe holds a notice with the word "forbidden" written on it, for he was not supposed to see anyone until the seven days of purification were completed.

the RIVeR kappa
and the ocean NINGYO

It was a lazy kind of day, and the lad Yoshi was drowsing
under a big willow tree when suddenly he heard a mighty splashing and the scream of a frightened horse. He jumped up, and
then scrambled behind the tree in alarm. Plunging from the
river, where it had evidently gone for a drink, was a wild-eyed
horse that Yoshi recognized as belonging to his neighbor. On
its neck and digging savagely into it was the strangest creature
the boy had ever seen. It had the body of a tortoise, legs of a
frog, face of a monkey, a pointed bill, and fierce little eyes that
seemed sharp enough to bore holes through rocks.

A Kappa! Yoshi knew all about Kappa, even though he had
never seen one before. A Kappa walks and talks like a real boy,
but nobody would want one for a playmate!

"Be very careful when you go by a river," his mother had
warned, "for it might be the home of a Kappa. Those malicious
creatures have a nasty trick of dragging children under water and
drowning them. If you meet one on land, it will demand that
you wrestle with it. Don't! Just bow as low as you can. A Kappa
is extremely polite. It will return your bow. If both of you bow
long and low enough, all the water will run out of the bowl-
shaped cavity on top of its skull and it will be harmless. Of course,
if you happen to have a cucumber along, that will help, for
Kappa are exceedingly fond of them."

Yoshi had remembered his mother's words so well that they
had given him any number of bad dreams, and sometimes when

no one was looking he practiced especially low bows, just to be on the safe side.

And here was one of those frightening creatures right before his eyes! But now the boy ventured cautiously from behind the tree, feeling a bit braver because the villagers, armed with clubs, were converging from all directions. Soon they had cornered the frenzied horse and tied up its fierce little rider.

"Kill the wicked water sprite before it does any more harm," someone shouted.

The owner of the horse came forward and lifted his club. Then he lowered it again. Such a quaint-looking thing this Kappa was and now, having lost all the water from its skull during that wild ride, it seemed as harmless as a toad. After all, it was no bigger than a ten-year-old boy and here was he, a grown man, about to kill it.

"If I let you go, will you promise to behave?"

The Kappa nodded so vigorously that its sharp little bill clattered.

"Will you sign a document?"

Again the creature bobbed its head.

Drawing out paper and ink, the man wrote in big black letters, "I, the Kappa of the Kawachi River, vow never again to disturb the inhabitants of this village or any of their animals."

"Now sign!" ordered the man.

"Can't write," answered the Kappa. Then, as the villagers surged forward, it added hastily, "Will this do?" It plunged a fist into the ink and daubed the paper.

The Kappa was released and the document taken to the temple for safekeeping. There it remains to this day. The Kappa kept its promise. Other people continue to be bothered with these dangerous water sprites, but the villagers by the Kawachi River, never.

The old fisherman just knew that something special was going to happen. Everything pointed to it. In the first place he had received some good news early in the morning—always a favorable sign. Then too, this was "great-peace day," which very often brings good luck.

He was right. Only a few moments after reaching his fishing grounds he felt a heavy tug at his net. When he had pulled it in, he squealed with joy. He had caught a Ningyo! An unusually beautiful one, too. She was about five feet long, he estimated, and her head and face were as pretty as those of a real woman. The skin had the translucent glow of a white jewel, and long black hair flowed luxuriantly down her back almost to the tip of her tail.

Such luck! The flesh of the Ningyo was a rare delicacy, for one who ate of it never grew older. Everyone knew about Yaobikuni, the girl who had eaten Ningyo flesh in her teens. For eight hundred years she had lived, always as young as on the day her father had given her the strange new food.

But as the fisherman drew his net onto the boat, he saw big tears come into the Ningyo's eyes. He paused. She was a fish, of course, but so much like a woman, despite that tail. And even the tail was pretty—all white and smooth, not a bit scaly like those of other fish. How could he destroy this delicate creature!

"Don't cry," he said gently. "I shall not harm you. See, I am going to let you return to your ocean home."

A smile luminous as sunset on water irradiated her face, and the tears still on her cheeks glistened with a pearly light. Why, they actually *were* pearls! The bottom of his boat was covered with her pearl-tears! Ecstatically the fisherman gathered them into his bamboo basket. But when he turned to thank the Ningyo who had made him rich for life, she had already slipped away into the sea.

Ningyo means "human fish." Reference to these mermaid-like beings is frequent in Japanese literature, and a temple in Wakasa Province has a statue of the girl who lived eight hundred years after having eaten Ningyo flesh. This octocentenarian, whose name means "800 years old," is listed in Japan's biographical dictionary.

To the Japanese there are lucky and unlucky days running in cycles through the year, and a careful person schedules important events for lucky ones only.

Almost every locality in Japan has stories about a Kappa, which means "river boy," drowning children or forcing someone to wrestle with it. But even if a person wins the wrestling bout he loses, for he becomes insane. The only real defense is to get the sprite to bow so low that the water runs out of the hole in its head. Curiously, Japan has several patent medicines said to have been invented by Kappa.

In some parts of Japan children throw cucumbers into the river before going for a swim to bribe Kappa not to harm them.

my lord bag of rice

When the warrior Hidesato was crossing a bridge over Lake
Biwa one day, he saw a dragon two hundred feet long lying fast
asleep in his path. Good-naturedly and without a moment's fear,
he leaped over it and went on his way. He had gone only a short
distance, however, when he heard someone call his name. Looking back he saw a red-haired man with a dragon-shaped crown
on his head. The dragon had disappeared.

"Honorable sir," said the man, bowing low, "I am the Dragon
King of Lake Biwa. Frequently I take my native form and lie
here on the bridge in the hope of discovering a truly brave
mortal. Today I found him. Others fled in terror when they
saw me in my dragon shape. You alone showed no fear."

"I am at your service," said Hidesato, sensing that here was
adventure, which—next to food—he liked best of all things in the
world.

"The mountain above Lake Biwa is the abode of a centipede
so huge that his body winds three times around the mountain.
At frequent intervals he crawls down and seizes my children and
grandchildren for food. Kill him for me! A warrior brave enough
to step over a dragon is brave enough to fight a centipede, even
one of this size."

Perilous adventure! This was better than ever! Readily Hidesato consented.

In the Dragon King's palace the warrior feasted on crystallized
lotus leaves and wine, and then was entertained by slant-eyed

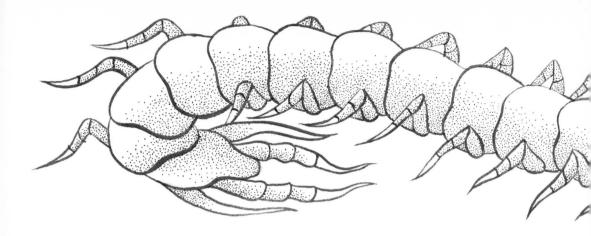

goldfish dancing to the strains of the koto played by ten white carp. It was all very satisfying, Hidesato reflected; probably not even the God of the Sea himself lived in a more sumptuous palace or could offer better entertainment than this Dragon King of Lake Biwa. A little excitement would help, though . . .

A crash interrupted his thoughts. Bounding to the door, he saw that the whole mountain above him was alive with the sinuous legs of a giant centipede. Tall trees bent like blades of grass under the bulging body. A careless flick of one hairy leg at an obstructing cliff sent it hurtling down into Lake Biwa. Two eyes like seething volcanos seemed to turn the low-hanging clouds to blood.

Hidesato fitted his arrow and gave a mighty tug at his bow. The missile struck the centipede squarely in the head but glanced off without halting for an instant that ponderous descent down the mountain. A second arrow too found its mark, and still the monster came on and on. This called for magic. Suddenly Hidesato remembered that human saliva has magical properties.

Into his mouth first and then into his bow went the next arrow. Straight into the centipede's brain it flew. A convulsive shudder shook the mountain as the magic began to work. The hundred legs tensed like gigantic traps; the volcanic fires flickered out of the eyes; the body swelled like an immense bellows for an instant and then collapsed with a blast of wind that leveled trees for miles. With a final spasm that rippled through hill and

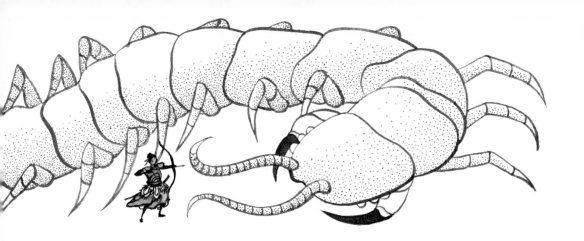

valley like earthquake, the monster crashed down the mountain into Lake Biwa.

The Dragon King's gratitude was boundless. Again he spread the finest delicacies of his kingdom before the valiant Hidesato and then presented him with four carefully wrapped gifts, the choicest treasures in the entire kingdom. Summoning a great company of fish, he changed them into a glittering retinue of attendants to escort the hero home in triumph.

When Hidesato examined his gifts he found a rice bag that was inexhaustible, a roll of silk that had no end, and a cooking pot that needed no fire. Very good gifts indeed, he reflected. The last present was a great bell. It was pretty, but as it appeared to have no magic properties, he promptly gave it to the temple at Miidera.

Now Hidesato was famous and rich, and since a bag of rice which never became empty seemed more practical than a centipede at the bottom of Lake Biwa, people called him "My Lord Bag of Rice" forever after.

Lakes in Japan are invariably associated with some legend concerning a dragon. Biwa, being a large lake, had a large dragon. This lake is shaped like the four-stringed Japanese lute, the biwa—hence its name.

The koto, a kind of harp, is the most aristocratic and difficult of all Japanese instruments. The samisen, which means "three-stringed," is probably the most popular one.

sukaru, the thunder catcher

Sukaru firmly believed that next to the emperor himself he was the smartest and most important person in Japan. In fact, his wife sometimes wondered if he got the order of importance mixed when he would boast, "I am the voice, eyes, and ears of His Majesty!"

Most people laughed at the fussy, self-important little man, but not the emperor! No other servant was so faithful, trustworthy, and hardworking as Sukaru. No job seemed too difficult for him. If he strutted a bit, what did it matter?

One day the emperor's young daughter was frightened during a violent thunderstorm and to soothe her the father said, "Do not fear the Thunder God, Little Princess. I'll make him go away soon." At that very moment in came Sukaru, looking for a job to do. "Better still," said the emperor, "I'll have Sukaru arrest the Thunder God for daring to come into my empire uninvited and make such a clamor."

Sukaru bowed low. "Your Majesty's orders shall be carried out at once," he said.

The emperor was giving him more important jobs every day, the little man reflected as he hurried away. This one would require more skill than usual, for he couldn't remember having heard of anyone catching the Thunder God before. But the deity had annoyed the emperor and naturally must be punished.

With a large sedan chair and a great number of drummers and horn blowers, Sukaru climbed the highest hill in the city.

Each time the thunder roared, the drummers and horn blowers made a mighty din and Sukaru would call, "Hear, hear, Thunder God. The emperor bids you come down immediately."

Now the Thunder God had assumed the shape of a dragon on this particular day and was riding about on the black clouds when he heard that imperious voice. Such impudence! This he would take care of quickly! Taking the form of a man, he came down to investigate. "Who dares to call the Thunder God?" he growled, expecting this puny creature to faint with fright. He didn't know Sukaru.

"Seize him!" shouted the little man, and at once the horn blowers and drummers grabbed the astonished Thunder God and tied him into the sedan chair. Then, holding his head even

higher than usual, Sukaru led the procession down the hill and back to the palace. "Your Majesty's order has been carried out," he said.

"What order?" said the emperor, who had completely forgotten his joke about arresting the Thunder God.

"The Thunder God is securely bound outside the gates. What shall I do with him now?"

The emperor really didn't know at the moment. This was an experience for which he had never been properly trained. But one look at the angry god fuming and thrashing about in the sedan chair helped him make up his mind.

"Take him back to the summit in haste and bid him return to the clouds!"

Sukaru bowed low. "At once, Your Majesty." Again the sedan chair, drummers, and horn blowers trailed up the hill behind the pompous servant.

The emperor called his chief priest immediately to make offerings to appease the angry Thunder God. But it was useless, for that very night Sukaru became ill. Nothing could be done for him, because this sickness was clearly the vengeance of the deity. Calling his children to his side Sukaru said, "I shall die before morning. Erect a tomb for me at the spot where I caught the Thunder God. So that people will always remember what a great man I was, inscribe on it these words:

> 'Here lies Sukaru,
> The Thunder-God Catcher.' "

He died, and the emperor decreed that the finest of funerals be given him. For seven days and nights the people went into mourning. Sukaru couldn't have arranged the ceremonies better himself.

Now the next time the Thunder God rumbled over the city, he was astounded to see the inscription on the tomb. Would that impertinent mortal never learn to behave himself? Hurling down a thunderbolt, he split the tomb into fragments. Sukaru was furious. His ghost leaped from the grave and yelled, "Come down and wrestle with me, Thunder God!" Assuming human shape, the deity came down to punish this insolent creature once and for all. But death hadn't lessened Sukaru's courage in the least. The little servant was a jujitsu expert, and soon it was the Thunder God who was being punished. Deftly the ghost flipped him onto his back and pinned him to the ground.

Attracted by the commotion, several men came running to the spot. "Dear, dear," they said; "this calls for some careful judgment. Send for His Majesty!"

Up the hill came the emperor. "My good servant," he said to the ghost, "do let the Thunder God go. If you will, I promise to build a new tomb for you, even better than the one he destroyed."

Sukaru, obedient to his master in death as in life, allowed the deity to scuttle back to the clouds. Bowing low, the ghost vanished into his grave.

Soon the new tomb with an improved inscription was erected. It read,

> "This is the tomb of Sukaru
> the Thunder Catcher. He caught
> the Thunder God once during his
> lifetime and once after his death."

114   The Thunder God never dared to bother Sukaru after that. To this day the summit on which the tomb stands is called Thunder Hill, and there is a saying

> Many are vain as Sukaru,
> But none so faithful and brave.

In Japanese art the Thunder God is pictured as a red-skinned man with the face of a demon, claws for hands, and with tiny clouds attached to his feet. He either carries drums on his back or drags them behind him in a bag at which mice are sometimes nibbling. Other pictures indicate that the Thunder God has just fallen from the skies, for his drums are broken and he is rubbing a bruised place on his body.

The Wind God, who also wears clouds on his feet, carries his winds in a bag, the extent to which he opens it determining whether a breeze or a hurricane will emerge. In art he is sometimes humorously depicted being swept away by the very winds he himself loosed.

Wind and bags seem to go together: Aeolus (ee' oh luss) in Greek myth likewise used a bag to imprison all contrary winds so that Odysseus could get home.

Trees struck by lightning in Japan cannot be cut down because they are considered sacred.

In Japan there is a saying that the five things to dread are thunder, earthquake, flood, fire, and Dad. Japanese fathers are evidently good disciplinarians.

visu and the fox-women

The woodman Visu was a hard worker, cutting wood from morning till night to keep enough food in the tiny hut for his wife and children—until the old priest visited him. "Visu," he said, "I'm afraid that you never pray."

"Too busy, much too busy," replied the woodman. "If you had a wife and family you wouldn't have time to pray either."

The priest's eyes flamed at this rude retort. "Think well what you say, man!" he said. "Do you not know that if you fail to respect the gods and their teachings that you may be reborn as a dog, a mouse, or even an insect?" Then the priest painted a vivid word-picture of the evils that could befall one so neglectful of the gods as Visu.

"Work *and* pray," said the priest as he departed. "Neither is adequate without the other."

From that day on, Visu was a changed man. Suddenly he found that he had no time for anything *except* prayer. His children became ragged and hungry; his wife, once so gentle and understanding, developed into a worried scold. "Rise, Visu, rise," she would cry. "You have been on your knees long enough; now use those strong arms with an axe in the woods so that there will be food for your little ones."

One day when his wife's words were especially hot, Visu lost his temper. "Woman," he said sternly, shaking a finger in her face, "the gods come first. I turn my back on your impiety!" He stormed from the hut and up the wooded slopes of Mount Fuji.

Muttering angrily to himself with every step, he climbed all day long. When at length he sat down to rest, he saw a fox dart through the thicket. On an impulse he followed it and shortly found himself in a small glen where two ladies were absorbed in the game of "Go." So intent were they on the little pegs which they moved about on the playing board that they paid no attention to Visu, despite his polite attempts to engage them in conversation. Fascinated both by their beauty and by the intricate game, Visu crept closer and closer to peer over their shoulders. He managed to keep quiet until one of the players made an unwise move. "No, no, fair lady," he cried; "you should have put the peg over there!" Instantly the women turned into foxes and scurried into the bushes. "Come back, come back," he called and then attempted to follow them.

Crack! He stopped, thunderstruck. Something had happened! His limbs creaked and his back groaned. Clutching painfully at one knee that had protested at his sudden movement, he saw that his strong hands looked like the knots of an ancient oak tree and that they were resting on a scraggly beard that drooped dejectedly to the ground.

"Woe, woe!" he wailed—and again he stopped. Why, he sounded like a cricket! What had happened to the lusty voice that once had resounded through the woods as he swung his axe?

Moaning in bewilderment, he shuffled down the mountain, his tears forming muddy little puddles down his long beard. Home! He must get home fast! But as he came to the clearing at the base of the mountain, he stopped short. Where *was* his home? Everything had changed. No hut, no woodpile, not even the clump of cedars that he had loved.

An old woman whom he had never seen before limped up the trail toward him, edging away uneasily as she tried to pass. "Wait," he cried. "I am Visu. Early this morning I climbed Mount Fuji, but nothing is as I left it."

"Visu!" she sniffed. "Everybody knows about that useless creature who stomped up the mountain in a temper three hundred years ago and never came back. His poor wife and children had a hard time of it, both before and after he went. Visu! Humph!"

Three hundred years? His wife and children! He had left them to starve! As he turned away and hobbled back toward the mountain, the old woman heard him mumble, "Work *and* pray. If you pray, you must work too."

Old Visu was never seen again, but it is said that on moonlit nights his spirit still haunts Fujiyama.

117

Japanese legend teems with stories of foxes which possess super-natural powers. Not only can they hear and understand everything, including one's thoughts, but they can transform themselves into any shape. Usually they choose the form of a beautiful woman who deludes and snares human beings as did the fox-women in this story.

The fox god, however, has attributes of both good and evil. Some-times he brings wealth, cures coughs, and helps children to bear the unusually hot baths of the Japanese. But more often he is cruel and to be feared.

It was this same Visu who, in his younger days, awoke one morning to find that on the barren plain before his hut a glorious mountain had sprung up over night. Smoke billowed from its crest, and opalescent clouds caressed its slopes. He named it "Fujiyama," which means "Never-dying Mountain." The volcano that Visu saw on its summit was for a long time extremely active. A final violent outbreak in 1707-1708 covered Tokyo, sixty miles away, with six inches of ash.

Fujiyama or Fujisan (both "yama" and "san" mean "mountain") is Japan's most beautiful and sacred mountain. It has been the inspiration for numerous artists through the centuries.

Because the grandson of the Sun Goddess first descended from heaven to a peak in southern Japan, mountains have always been particularly revered. Climbing them is in itself an act of worship, and they are the most frequent sites for shrines.

"Go" is a highly popular game somewhat like checkers but far more complicated. It is said that a Japanese envoy to China was once asked to play it. Not knowing the game, he was embarrassed. But an accom-modating spider came down from the ceiling and instructed him.

kwannon and the hermit

On the heights of Mount Nariai overlooking a jeweled bay lived an old hermit. Though his food, clothing, and shelter were coarse and meager, he considered himself the most blessed of men because of the beauty that filled his eyes and heart each time he emerged from his tiny hut and looked down on the panorama of sea, wooded hill, and promontory below.

He had built a shrine to Kwannon, Goddess of Mercy, and during the summer months many people from the village below made their way up the mountain to pray in this sacred spot. They loved and honored the old hermit because in his kind face they saw the goodness that they were trying to bring into their own lives.

But during the winter months the hermit was cut off from everyone because the snow often lay twenty feet deep. Yet, no matter how difficult the task, he always tried to force his way to the shrine of his beloved goddess every day.

One year when the storms were unusually severe, the old man was confined to his hut for a long time. At last his meager food supply was gone. Weak with hunger, he pushed open his door one morning to find a deer frozen to death in the nearby drifts.

His first thought being a prayer of gratitude, he started to drag the animal into his hut. Then he stopped. Well he knew that it was offensive to Kwannon to eat the flesh of animals. Yet, would the merciful goddess have him starve while food lay right before him? If he died here in the snow, no longer could he be a source of inspiration to the people who trudged up the mountain year after year to his sanctuary.

He made his decision. Cutting off a piece of venison, he cooked and ate enough to renew his strength. The rest he left in his cooking pot.

In time the sun cast its long sparkling tendrils over the snow and melted it sufficiently to allow some of the more hardy villagers to ascend the mountain. Sadly they toiled up the slopes, fearing that their good hermit had perished in the storm. But when they reached his hut, the sound of his voice—clear and strong as he chanted praises to Kwannon—came to their ears.

"A frozen deer saved me from starvation," he told them. "See, here in my cooking pot is the part of the animal that I did not eat."

Several of the villagers looked inside the vessel. "But this is not venison," said one. "This is only a piece of wood."

A cry came from a youth who had gone up to the shrine. "Look! The image of the goddess is no longer whole!" It was true; a piece was missing.

"But see," said another, "the wound is the size of the wood in the cooking pot." Reverently they put the wood in the gaping hole and it slipped into place, making the image complete once more.

Then they understood. The frozen deer was the gentle Kwannon herself who, in her infinite mercy and love, had given a part of her body that the revered old priest might live.

Kwannon, often called the Japanese Madonna, is one of the most beloved of all the Buddhist deities. She is the subject of many stories, and artists find her a constant source of inspiration. One tapestry depicting her has become famous. It shows Kwannon as the Divine Mother pouring forth the holy water of creation, in each bubble of which is a tiny baby. The creator of this exquisite work of art used twelve thousand different shades of silk and twelve kinds of gold thread. Three years went into its making.

the sacred crystal

120   Excitement rippled through every room, court, and garden of Kamatari's palace. For into his courtyard had come messengers bearing yellow silk banners embroidered with dragons—emblem of the Emperor of China.

Bowing low before Kamatari, the imperial ambassadors said, "Our illustrious emperor has heard of the beauty of your daughter Kohaku Jo and wishes to marry her."

"We are honored," said Kamatari, hardly able to believe this good fortune. "She shall prepare at once to go to China."

"Furthermore," continued the ambassador, "our emperor bids us tell you that when the maiden becomes empress she will be permitted to choose whatever gifts she wishes from the vast treasure stores of China to send back to Japan."

Kohaku Jo bowed her head and quick tears fell to her silken robe as she listened to these words. Yes, a very great honor indeed, but how could she bear to leave beautiful Japan for the distant land across the sea, never again to see her loved ones? Sadly the young girl crept away to the temple where she had been blessed as a baby. "Protect and help me," she prayed to the goddess, "and I will promise to send three precious gifts from China as a thank offering."

Feeling comforted and secure in the love of the deity, Kohaku Jo made the journey to China. The emperor received her with kindness and proceeded at once to escort her through his many palaces that she might see the magnificence of the realm into which she had come. But proud though he was of his treasures, he knew that his young empress was lovelier than any of them. "The royal goldsmith shall make a special pathway through the gardens so that her exquisite feet need never touch the earth," he decreed. "Its stepping stones of gold and silver shall be

shaped like lotus leaves. They will endure forever as symbols of her beauty."

All these splendors, however, reminded Kohaku Jo even more sharply of her promise to send back to Japan three gifts for the temple. "Let me fulfill my vow," she said to the emperor. "Only then can I enjoy the delights of this kingdom."

Marvelously carved chests were brought before the young empress at once. In silent wonder she examined their treasures. How could she select from so many the three gifts that would be most pleasing to her beloved goddess! Finally she chose a musical instrument that would play celestial strains forever, an inkstone box with an inexhaustible supply of Indian ink, and—most wonderful of all—a crystal that would bring unending peace of soul to whoever looked at it. Within its depths was a statuette of Buddha on a white elephant, and the radiance that enfolded him seemed like a vision of paradise.

The emperor selected his finest ship to carry these gifts to Japan. "Guard them well," he admonished the captain, "for they are the fulfillment of a sacred vow."

The vessel sailed on serene waters until it had nearly reached the shores of Japan close to Kohaku Jo's old home. But suddenly a tempest arose. Shrieking waves tossed the ship about like a toy. Lightning and thunder lacerated the heavens. Then, so quickly that it seemed as if a master's quiet hand had stilled an angry beast, the storm was gone. But the precious crystal had disappeared.

Hastening to land, the distressed captain informed Kamatari, Kohaku Jo's father, of the loss. Wise in the ways of the sea, Kamatari knew at once what had happened. "The Dragon King of the Sea possesses two magic jewels that control the ebb and flow of the tide," he said. "He is covetous of all other gems. He caused the tempest so that he could snatch the crystal from the ship Someone must go down to the Dragon Palace to regain the stolen treasure."

Because he knew that his daughter would be heartbroken if she could not keep her promise to the goddess, Kamatari offered rich rewards to anyone who would attempt the hazardous task of finding the crystal. But though many men tried, all failed.

Then a poor shell-gatherer with a baby in her arms came up to Kamatari. "Let me search," she begged. "If I succeed, reward

me with your promise to bring up my little son as your own that he may become more in life than a fisher lad."

Touched by her concern for her child, Kamatari consented, though he had little hope that this frail woman could succeed where strong men had failed. She tied a rope around her waist, fastened a knife to it, gave the end to a fisherman standing by, and plunged into the sea. Down and down she swam until the coral towers of the Dragon King's palace came into view. On the topmost pinnacle she saw a shimmering light whose rays spread out through the ocean like an immense fan made of moonbeams. It was the crystal! But how was she to get it? On every side were dragons, guardians of the treasure.

Gliding noiselessly into the very midst of the great creatures, whose baleful eyes lolled in sleep, she snatched the crystal. At once the dragons awoke and, in a violent clamor of thrashing tails, pursued her. She could not hope to outdistance them; in another moment they would be upon her. But she knew that dragons were mortally afraid of blood. Ripping out the knife tied to her waist, she cut a deep wound into her breast and thrust the crystal into the gaping hole. Blood gushed about her in a crimson pool as she swam on and on. The dragons recoiled at the sight and turned back.

When the fishermen pulled her out of the sea and laid her on the sand, they thought that she was dead. But for a moment she opened her eyes, withdrew the crystal from her bleeding breast, and murmured, "Your promise, Kamatari!"

"I shall remember," he vowed. Then the woman fell back dead.

Under Kamatari's loving care the child grew up to become a famous statesman. Learning of his mother's heroism, he erected a temple in her honor on the Bay of Shidonoura. There it stands to this day, and pilgrims still visit it to pay respect to the woman who sacrificed so bravely for her son.

The crystal was placed in the temple where Kohaku Jo had knelt in prayer. The Empress of China had fulfilled her vow.

the goddess Benten

One day when the handsome young poet Baishu was attending a festival, the wind blew to his feet a piece of paper on which was written a poignant little love poem, a tanka. He could not see where it had come from, but he put it in his pocket and went home.

The poem didn't stay in his pocket, though. All evening he took it out and read it again and again. With each reading he became more enchanted. He felt certain that only a very sensitive, gentle girl could have expressed her thoughts so charmingly and written them in such graceful Japanese characters. Even the ink, so fresh and clear, seemed to suggest that an unusually delicate hand had been using it. Day by day he became more interested in the unknown girl who had composed the poem. He must find her!

The Goddess Benten was kind to lovers. Perhaps she would help him. To her temple he went. "Gracious Goddess," he prayed, "let me find the girl who wrote this tanka, for she alone can I love." Seven times he came to the temple. On the seventh night an old man in ceremonial robes entered and knelt close beside him. Then the outer door opened and a bamboo curtain was raised to reveal a handsome boy. "We have heard the pleas of a youth who has fallen in love," he said to the old man. "You are to bring the two young people together."

The old man bowed low and drew from his sleeve a cord, which he wound about Baishu's body. Igniting one end of the cord in a lantern, he waved his hand as if beckoning to someone. A girl entered the temple, her face half concealed by a fan. As she knelt beside Baishu, he heard the boy behind the bamboo curtain murmur, "We have heard your prayers. The maiden you love is at your side." In that instant the boy, the girl, and the old man were gone.

The wondering Baishu started home. On the way a slender figure slipped to his side. It was the girl he had seen in the temple. He spoke, and in the gentle voice with which she replied he seemed to hear echoes of the love poem that had captured his heart. Placing her hand in his she said quietly, "The Goddess Benten has made me your wife."

In the days that followed, Baishu was enfolded in golden mists of complete happiness. The poem had spoken truly of its creator, for her every glance and movement brought new grace and beauty into being. His home soon reflected her charm in exquisite flower arrangements, embroideries, and paintings. Occasionally he was a little puzzled that his neighbors seemed unaware of his wife's presence and that she never mentioned her family, but his joy in her left no room for disturbing thoughts. She had come to him from the gracious Goddess Benten and was his to love forever. That was all he needed to know.

Then a strange thing happened.

He was walking one day in a distant part of the city when a servant came from one of the large houses and said respectfully, "My master wishes to see you. Please follow me." Baishu hesitated for only a moment, a compelling urge making him do as he was asked.

Inside the house a kindly man greeted him and said, "Forgive me for bringing you here in this unusual manner, but I am acting under the guidance of the Goddess Benten. Last night she spoke to me in a dream and said that she had found the man who should marry my daughter. The goddess described him so minutely that when I saw you pass I knew that you were the one. Come, my daughter is waiting for you."

Baishu was filled with distress. How could he explain to this confident, trusting man that he was already married? Yet, almost without realizing it, he followed his host into another room.

"This is she," said the father proudly, and Baishu looked into the eyes of his own beloved wife! Yes, it was unmistakably she, and yet there was a difference...

Out of the youth's love came understanding. Suddenly he knew that the girl who had come to him in the temple was the soul of his wife and that the smiling girl before him was her body. The goddess had wrought the miracle to bring together two young people whose hearts could communicate in the language of poetry, beauty, and love.

Perhaps in no other country has poetry entered so intimately into the lives of people as in Japan. Almost everyone learns to compose the little verses called tanka and haiku. Japanese literature indicates that it was not at all unusual to fall in love through a poem, just as Baishu did. In fact, poetry acted as a go-between in love affairs. Japan's famous tenth-century novel The Tale of Genji contains hundreds of tanka, whole conversations being carried on in this thirty-one syllable verse form.

Benten—goddess of love, beauty, music, and one of the seven deities of good luck—is worshipped at many shrines along the coast. As she is the daughter of the Dragon King, her most famous shrine, which is on an island of the Inland Sea, suggests the undersea palace from which she came. Its buildings and galleries stand on a sandy beach where the tide rises so high that the shrine seems to be floating on water. Rows of iron lanterns illuminate the sea and cast a glow on rocky heights looming behind the temple. The island upon which this shrine rests is pointed out to tourists as the place where there is neither birth nor death. Benten's musical instrument is the biwa. She is represented in art as riding on either a dragon or a serpent.

the jewel tears

One day a youth named Totaro was crossing a long bridge at Seta when he saw an odd-looking creature huddled against the railing. It was like, and yet curiously unlike a man. The enormous eyes seemed to be liquid emeralds and the beard was that of a dragon. But he looked so forlorn that Totaro's heart was touched.

"What can I do for you," he asked.

The man looked at him dolefully, and the emerald eyes rolled in their sockets. "My name is Samebito, and I am most miserable. A few days ago I was a trusted retainer in the Palace of the Dragon King. But because of a petty mistake I was dismissed and banished from the kingdom. Now here I am, without either food or shelter, and so lonely."

"Come with me," said Totaro. "I have a pool and a waterfall in my garden, and food in my house. You are welcome to both."

Gratefully Samebito followed him home and soon was splashing happily in the pool and sliding down the waterfall. And when Totaro came out with some raw fish for supper, the fellow bowed so low in gratitude that his beard dusted the ground.

About six months later Totaro attended a festival at the temple of Miidera, and there he saw a girl with the fragile loveliness of springtime's first flowers and a voice like that of the nightingale. He fell in love at once and sought out the parents to ask her hand in marriage.

"Our daughter Tamana will wed only the man who can give her ten thousand jewels," they told him.

Totaro crept home, too heartbroken to enjoy the festivities any longer. He went to his room and stayed there for days, unable to eat, drink, or sleep. Without Tamana he wanted nothing but to wither away and die.

Samebito missed his kind master, and one morning he left his pool and slipped into the house. When he saw Totaro lying pale and listless under the coverlet, scarcely breathing, the little man fell down on his knees and wept. Big red tears rolled down his cheeks. One of them fell with a sharp smack on Totaro's hand, and the dying youth saw with amazement that it was a glowing ruby. He sat upright. All around Samebito lay the precious jewels, because the little man's grief for his master was great.

"I am saved!" cried Totaro. "Oh, Samebito, now I can marry Tamana!"

Joyfully he began to count the jewels, sorting them into piles of one hundred each. But the last pile was not complete. "Dear Samebito," he cried, "do weep some more!"

But the little man was sitting back on his heels, mystified at his master's strange behavior. He shook his head. "I do not understand. You were sick, and I wept. Now you are well, and you want me still to weep! This is a time for rejoicing!"

"But you must weep again," cried Totaro, " for only then can I win the beautiful Tamana. It was for love of her that I became ill, and without her I shall become ill again. So please weep again, Samebito!"

The little man was insulted. "I cannot cry like a foolish woman over nothing!" he sniffed. Then, as he saw his master's crestfallen face, he said gently, "Tomorrow let us go to Seta Bridge where you found me. Perhaps as I try to catch a glimpse of my old home, I can weep again."

Early next morning they set out for the bridge. Samebito leaned against its railing and looked over the waters. In his mind's eye he saw again the crystal turrets of the Dragon King's palace and the bright gardens where trees bore jewels instead of fruit. Loneliness for that splendid kingdom welled into his heart, and the hot tears began to flow.

He was aroused from his pensive reverie by Totaro's happy cry. "You can stop weeping now, Samebito, for I have the ten thousand rubies."

The little man turned sadly to his master, and then his eyes began to glow like the jewels that he had wept. "Listen!" he cried. "Do you hear?"

"I hear nothing," said Totaro. "Come, let us leave, for I must go at once to Tamana with my casket of jewels."

"They are calling me!" exulted Samebito. "I have been forgiven! Look!"

From the waters came the sound of music, and a palace of rainbow mist appeared on the ocean waves. Samebito sprang to the parapet of the bridge. "Farewell, good master," he said. "The Dragon King has relented and welcomes me back to my ocean home!"

Into the sea he plunged, and the waves enfolded him.

the listening cap

"I have nothing left to offer but myself. Take my life, if you will have it!"

The man praying before the shrine of his beloved guardian god was old and poor. There was nothing left to eat in his small hut. Yet his greatest concern was not his hunger but that he no longer had any gift to place before the shrine.

As he knelt there, a murmur and then a soft voice came to him from far away. "Kind old man," it said, "do not grieve. Beside you is a magic listening cap. Wear it and you will understand the language of butterflies, flowers, and all living creatures—even of the springtime itself. You will hear the gentle speech of autumn leaves and of the nightingale as it rejoices in the loveliness of plum blossoms."

The voice died away, but there beside the old man was a little red cap. He put it on and started home. On the way he stopped to rest under a comfortable tree. There his attention was attracted by two crows, one coming from the mountains and the other from the sea. As they chatted in the branches above him, he heard one say, "I have been away for a long time. Tell me, how is my friend, the little camphor tree?"

"He is most unhappy," sighed the other crow. "Some time ago a wealthy man cut him down in order to build a guest house in the garden, but he did not dig out the roots. Now each time our friend sends out new shoots from beneath the house, they are removed by the gardener. The tree moans and begs for mercy, but human beings are too insensitive to hear his plaintive cries. Unless he is dug up soon and transplanted to a spot where there is room for him to grow, he will surely die. What is more, the master of the house is ill too, for he was responsible for the tree's agonies and thus a spell has been cast upon him. When our friend the camphor dies, so will the master."

The old man snatched off his cap, unable to bear any more. He must save both the tree and the master. But how? Who would believe him if he were to say that he had overheard the conversation of two crows! He must think of some clever scheme. Perhaps if he were to disguise himself as a fortune teller...

The next day he went to town and strolled up and down the street calling, "Fortunes! I tell fortunes!" The wife of the sick man came running out. "Please come in and see if you can determine what ails my poor husband," she cried.

"Allow me to sleep in your guest house tonight," he requested, "and tomorrow I will be able to help you."

"Gladly," said the wife, and she prepared a soft bed for him.

When all was quiet that night, the old man put on his listening cap. Excited little rustles came from all around as the grasses and

flowers and trees conversed about the events of the day. But from underneath the floor came a desolate moan. Then a voice asked, "Are you feeling any better tonight, Little Camphor Tree?"

"Is that you, Pine Tree? No, I grow weaker. I think I am about to die."

Then another whisper: "It is I, the Cedar. Be brave, Little Camphor. Perhaps help will come soon."

One after another of the garden trees murmured sympathetically to their unhappy friend and tried to comfort him by crooning tenderly to the accompaniment of the breeze that played in their branches.

The next morning the old man went to the bedside of the dying master. "Dig up the camphor tree whose roots languish beneath your guest house. Remove it to a sunny part of your garden, and you will become well."

Gardeners transplanted the camphor that very day, and the happy little tree sang in ecstasy. "Now I can breathe and see again the blue of sky and gold of sun. Ah, my friends, this must be the most delightful garden in the whole world!" And all the trees and flowers rejoiced in the happiness of the camphor.

The master recovered quickly and in gratitude rewarded the old man with three bags full of gold coins. Now there would always be enough food in the tiny hut and offerings for the shrine as well. Not being greedy, the old man never again tried to tell fortunes. Very often, however, he put on his listening cap just to share the joys and sorrows of the flowers, fireflies, and myriads of other living creatures whose speech he alone could understand.

Melampus (me lamp′ us) in Greek mythology learned to understand the speech of animals, birds, and trees too. His magic gift came when some snakes he had befriended licked his ears as he slept in the garden.

a BOUQUET OF MAGIC

People were in a turmoil. Night after night some strange wild animal came into their gardens, trampling the flowers, breaking branches from trees, and ruining the graceful miniature bridges and waterfalls. Even the carefully cultivated rice fields were being ravaged.

No barriers were strong enough to hold the creature out, and it seemed to go almost everywhere at once. Could so much damage be done by only one enemy? The villagers organized themselves into groups to watch for the intruder, but no one could catch so much as a glimpse of it.

Then one moonlit night a sleepless little boy crept into the garden. There, carved against the silver of the night, was a great black horse. For one moment the animal looked at him and then leaped over the garden wall. Clambering up the gate, the boy was just in time to see the horse melt into the shadows of a temple far down in the valley.

"I have seen him!" he called to his parents. "It is a black stallion who has been destroying our gardens and fields. Come, I will show you where he went!"

The neighbors were aroused, and soon an excited group was following the lad down the winding path to the temple. Into the sacred building he led them. Yes, a black horse was there, but it was only a long-familiar painting on a wall. Never had the villagers seen it like this, however, for it was steaming and panting as if from violent exertion.

"Why, it is the horse in Kanasoka's painting that comes down each night to destroy our fields and gardens!" said a villager.

"Look, it still has fresh greens about its mouth!" said another.

"But what can we do about a painted steed that comes alive?"

"Only the artist himself can make his creation behave. Send for Kanasoka!"

Early next morning the artist came to the temple. Deftly he painted in a tethering rope and a sturdy post. Thus firmly attached, the horse stayed where he belonged in the picture and never again bothered the villagers.

The lad Sesshu was misbehaving. He had entered the temple to become a priest. Dutifully he learned the prayers and chanted Buddhist scriptures, the sutras, as long as his teachers were around. But as soon as he was left alone, out came his brush and paints and then he was lost in a dreamy world of his own creation.

"Careful, Sesshu," warned the patient head priest. "Do not let the things of this world make you forget why you are in the temple!"

"I will try, Master," said the youth humbly. But the urge to paint was too strong. "Just a few minutes now and then cannot hurt," he told himself. But minutes had a disconcerting way of stretching into hours, and very soon he was neglecting his prayers again.

At length the head priest became annoyed. "I must discipline you, Sesshu." Taking the boy to a far room of the temple, he bound him to a pillar. "Here you shall stay alone tonight," he said sternly. "Perhaps then it will be easier for you to remember that you must keep your brush and paints out of sight."

The boy was terrified. How could he endure to stay in this place alone till morning! The tears fell hot and fast, for he was still a small lad, and soon a puddle had formed on the floor. Like paint, thought Sesshu; now, if he just had a brush...

His hands were bound, but feet were free. Off came the wooden clogs, and with his toes and tears the boy drew a picture of two rats on the floor. Scarcely was the last whisker finished when the creatures yawned, stretched, and began to frisk about the room. For a while they had so much fun in this nice new world that they didn't even notice Sesshu. Then they caught sight of his tear-stained face. Too bad! and such a nice little fellow!

Scurrying back to the lad, the rats gnawed industriously at the ropes. Strand after strand snapped under their sharp teeth—for Sesshu was a very careful painter—until at last the boy was free. "Thank you," he whispered, and then crept from the room back to his own cosy bed where he belonged.

✤

The maiden Saijosen was so skillful at embroidery that people came from afar to see her tapestries. One day as she was working, an old man came and sat beside her. For a long time he said nothing, so absorbed was he in the vivid pictures unfolding on the cloth before him. When Saijosen had nearly finished, he spoke: "It is almost perfect. But could you now work a pair of phoenixes into this corner?" Good-naturedly Saijosen consented.

The tapestry completed, the artist turned to the old man for approval. He closed his eyes for a moment and then pointed at the birds. Their wings began to flutter and their heads to arch. Then they stepped down from the tapestry. Seating themselves on the birds, Saijosen and the old man soared away into the heavens.

The phoenix is a sacred bird that, like the dragon, appears frequently in Japanese painting, sculpture, and ceramics. Artists depict it as having feathers of five colors, head of a cock, neck of a snake, back of a turtle, and tail of a fish. The ancient Chinese, from whom the Japanese borrowed the idea of the phoenix, believed that the bird came into the country only when a wise monarch was on the throne.

Kanasoka and Sesshu were famous artists of old Japan.

In Greek myth the maiden Arachne (ah rack' nee), like Saijosen, could embroider tapestries of superlative beauty. Arachne was changed into a spider because she dared to compete with Athena, goddess of weaving.

the avenging fireflies

Old Kanshiro was a devout pilgrim. All year long he sacrificed so that each summer he could visit the sacred shrines at Ise to ask blessings and to honor the gods with offerings. At last, however, he became so feeble that he was certain he would have strength for only one more journey. The villagers, who revered the old man for his unfailing piety, contributed small sums of money so that he could present gifts to the deities on this final visit.

Putting the coins in a small bag around his neck, Kanshiro set off for the distant province. But on the way he became ill and was obliged to stay at a small inn for several days. "Keep my money safe for me," he said to his host Jimpachi.

When the old man had recovered somewhat and was on his way again, he discovered that the coins had been taken from his bag and replaced with rocks. Back he trudged to the innkeeper. "Please return my money," he pleaded. "It is the gift of my friends and neighbors to the deities of Ise."

"You are an impudent old one to accuse me of stealing!" Jimpachi said. "Out with you!" With that he struck the old man and drove him from the inn.

Painfully Kanshiro resumed his journey and arrived at last, hungry and exhausted, at the sacred shrines. But he could offer only his humble prayers: there were no gifts to place before his beloved gods. When he returned home, he sold his meager possessions to repay the money contributed by his neighbors for the shrines. Now he was so poor that he was forced to beg for a living.

Some time later Kanshiro again passed through the village where he had been so cruelly treated. There he found that the innkeeper had become rich and powerful. "You took the gifts intended for sacred shrines," said Kanshiro, "and some day you shall suffer for your evil."

"Again you dare accuse me!" said Jimpachi. Then he called to his servants: "Drive this miserable beggar away, but first give him such a beating that he will never come back!"

They carried out the order only too well, for that night Kanshiro died. A kind priest at the outskirts of the village burned his body in the temple and said prayers for his soul.

When the innkeeper Jimpachi heard of the old man's death, he was terrified. Echoes of the words predicting punishment for his theft and cruelty rang in his ears, and visions of the old man pleading for the money passed like ominous shadows before his eyes. He became ill with worry, and horrid dreams drove sleep away. Day and night he tossed in fever, unable to find peace either of body or spirit.

Then one morning the villagers saw a glittering wave of fireflies come out of Kanshiro's tomb. Straight to Jimpachi's home they flew and swarmed over the mosquito netting around his bed. Servants and neighbors tried to drive them away, but on they came in ever-increasing numbers until the room glowed with eerie firefly light. Little by little the mosquito netting sank under the weight of the insects until it lay on Jimpachi like a suffocating shroud. And still the gleaming hordes came.

"The vengeance of Kanshiro!" cried the onlookers. In terror they fled from the firefly-choked room.

Then the mosquito netting ripped apart under its burden of angry insects, and they flew into the nose and eyes of the screaming Jimpachi. For days they continued to come until their massed bodies were like a glittering bridge arched between Kanshiro's tomb and the bedside of the sick man.

When at last the innkeeper died, the fireflies rose into the air and disappeared. Kanshiro was avenged.

138

the Boy who Bought a dream

A youth was sauntering along a country road one fine morning
when he came across a friendly old man. "Let's walk together
and enjoy each other's company," he suggested. The old man
gladly accepted the invitation but very soon was forced to stop.
"Your young legs travel too fast for me," he said. "Can we not
rest for a few moments under this shady tree before continuing
our journey?"

The good-natured youth consented, and within a few minutes
his companion had fallen fast asleep.

Suddenly the boy was startled to see a bee crawl out of the old
man's ear, circle about for a few moments, and then fly out over
the water to a nearby island. But soon it came back, flitted about
the sleeper's face and then winged into the sky.

When the old man awoke he said, "So strange a dream!"

"Was it about a bee?" asked the youth.

"Yes, but how did you know? I dreamed that one came to me
from that small island, took me there and showed me a white
camellia bush glorious with blossoms. 'If you dig at the roots,'
it said, 'you will find gold.'"

"And in your dream, did you find the gold?"

"That I did, and soon became the richest lord in the land."

The youth was silent for a while and then he said, "Look here,
old man, I'd like to buy that dream from you."

"Buy a dream?" chuckled his companion. "I've told it to you
and thus it is yours already."

"No," insisted the other, "it isn't mine until I pay for it. Will this be enough money?" With that he emptied all the coins he had into the old man's hand.

"More than enough. I hope you will enjoy my dream!"

They parted, and the youth went at once to the island and secured work from the rich lord dwelling there. Patiently he waited through fall and winter for the springtime that would bring camellias into bloom.

When at last the air was fragrant and warm, he eagerly tramped through the hills behind the lord's estate, searching for the spot described in the dream. Often his heart sang with hope as he caught the far-off gleam of snowy blooms. But always disappoint-

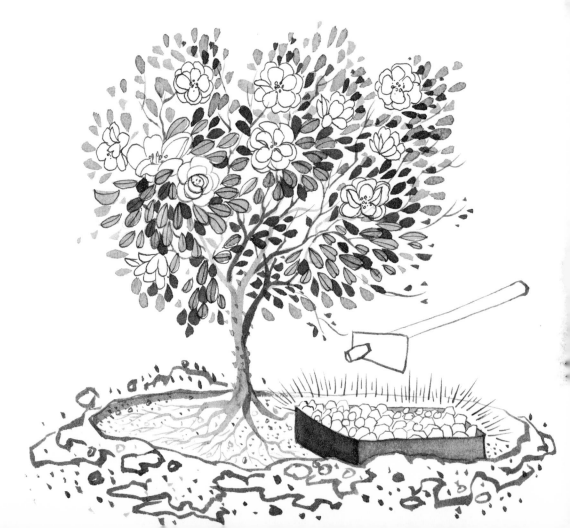

ment awaited him. He found many white blossoms, but they weren't camellias—and many camellia bushes with blossoms, but they weren't white. It was most vexing.

Summer days melted into crisp autumn and fairy-fingered winter, and the dream had to be tucked away for a while. But when the Princess Who Makes The Flowers To Bloom had again adorned hillside, dell, and quiet lane with freshly arranged bouquets, the youth resumed his search. Never for a moment had he lost sight of the dream.

At last, in a wooded glen he saw the tree, its sunlit blossoms trembling in the breeze. He dug around the roots. There it was— a box brimming with gold!

"Such a good dream," he mused happily as he crammed the treasure into his knapsack, "the best one, I am sure, that anyone ever bought."

141

One must be careful about selling dreams, or he may be duped as was an innocent young girl who sold one that would have made her the most important lady in Japan. She came to her sister Masako one morning and told her of a puzzling dream she had just had. Pretending to be distressed, the deceitful Masako said, "You must sell this dream quickly or it will come true—and it is a bad one indeed." "How can I?" asked the girl. "Just give your consent, and I will buy it." The transaction was made. That very morning a letter came from a great prince who had fallen in love with the girl. But because she had sold her dream, the letter was delivered to her sister instead. Thus it was Masako who married the prince and became the great lady.

And then there is the story of a man who dreamed he was changed into a butterfly. When he awoke the dream remained so vivid that he was never quite sure whether he was a man who had dreamed of being a butterfly or a butterfly dreaming he was a man.

Bad dreams come to just the end they deserve: the Baku—a mythical animal with the trunk of an elephant, two tusks, a spotted hide, and the tail of an ox—eats them! They are his sole article of diet. At one time it was customary to hang pictures of the Baku in houses and to write his name on pillows that the creature might be handy in case of a nightmare, for when a Baku ate a bad dream he had the power to change it to good luck.

the girl with
the bowl on her head

A poor widow, knowing that she was soon to die, said to her
daughter Hachihime, "I worry about your future, Little One, for
you have become very beautiful. To a young girl who has no one
to protect her, beauty can be a curse. When I am gone, promise
that you will wear this lacquered wooden bowl over your head
so that your face may be hidden."

Unhesitatingly Hachihime consented, realizing that the odd
request was born of her mother's deep devotion.

Soon afterward the widow died, and the girl placed the bowl
upon her head as she had promised. Now she was forced to earn
her own living, and she found work in the rice fields. Her quaint
appearance caused much jesting and laughing, and soon she became known throughout the country as the "girl with a bowl on
her head." Many a young worker in the fields beside her vowed
he would remove the clumsy object, but something in her quiet,
assured manner always made him change his mind and back
away, troubled.

The wealthy farmer for whom she worked began to notice that
she was unusually quick and careful, and he decided to bring her
into his house to care for his sick wife. Her gentleness and
industry won their hearts, and they came to cherish her as if she
were their own child.

When the farmer's son returned home from the gay capital
of Kyoto where he had been studying, he was highly amused
by the strange-looking girl. He tried to persuade her to remove

the bowl, but she only shook her head and went quietly on with her work. His curiosity aroused, the youth found himself strolling often into the kitchen to talk with her. Gradually his amusement gave way to interest and then to love.

"I wish to marry the girl with the bowl on her head," he told his startled father. "The bowl hides her face, but it cannot hide the beauty of her nature."

Dubiously the father consented, but when the news was revealed to the relatives, they were indignant. "She is a scheming young thing who wears that silly object just to pique your interest," they told the youth. "Never can we welcome such a one as she into our family!"

From that moment on Hachihime was ridiculed more than ever, and now ugly spite was added to her burden. Even the farmer's wife whom she had nursed so tenderly became suspicious and unkind. But the son fell more deeply in love with her every

day and persisted in his determination to marry her. At last his mother and relatives, seeing that it was impossible to dissuade him, agreed to accept her. "But he will be sorry, foolish boy!" they predicted darkly.

Then new difficulties arose, for the maiden herself refused him. "I am only a serving girl with no marriage portion," she said. "I cannot become a rich man's bride." His earnest pleas brought only that sad, quiet shake of her head.

But that night when her tears had ceased to flow and she had fallen asleep, her mother appeared in a dream. "Marry him, Little One, and all will be well with you." Shyly Hachihime told the youth of her dream the next morning, and he started at once to make marriage preparations.

When all the wedding guests were assembled, they began to murmur among themselves: "Was there ever such a queer-looking bride as this? Surely she will take that ridiculous bowl off now!" She too felt certain that the time had come to remove it. Try as she would, however, she was unable to do so. The relatives also tugged at it, punctuating their efforts with cruel comments, but suddenly the bowl began to make strange sounds that sent them scuttling away in alarm.

Then the bridegroom said, "The ceremony will go on, Little One. With or without the bowl, you are precious to me."

Silently they sipped the rice wine three times from each of three red lacquered cups. The very moment that the ceremony was completed, the wooden bowl splintered into pieces and dropped to the floor. From it rained gold, silver, and precious stones.

"My marriage portion! Now, my husband, I do not come to you empty handed!"

She knelt to run her fingers through the treasure at her feet. But the guests and bridegroom had eyes only for the maiden, because they saw that the wooden bowl had been concealing the most beautiful face in Japan.

A Japanese wedding usually takes place at the groom's house, to which the bride comes dressed in white, the Shinto color of mourning. For the ceremony she changes to a black robe richly ornamented with the family crest and other designs. Silently the bride and groom sip rice wine from three red bowls until each has been used three times, a total of nine. Then they offer wine to the parents and guests, and the ceremony is over. Some modern weddings take place in the banquet halls of large department stores. But wherever performed, the important moment is the ritual drinking of the rice wine by the couple.

the mirror of matsuyama

146   The child and her mother were pleased when the father told them that he had to journey to faraway Kyoto. Of course they would miss him, but he would come back with delightful stories about the wonders of the capital city. Besides, he was certain to bring a present for each of them.

They were right. When he returned, they sat down on the white mats and eagerly watched him open his basket. For the child there were tiny rice cakes and a doll so lifelike it seemed about to speak. The mother's gift was puzzling at first. It was round and flat, shiny on one side and decorated on the other with pine trees and long-legged storks.

"It is a mirror," her husband explained, feeling important that he had learned so much in the big city, for no one in this remote village had ever seen a mirror before. "The picture here is just a reflection of your own sweet face."

Thanking him prettily, the mother wrapped up the gift in her best green silk and put it away. This was a treasure to be used only on special festival days, she decided.

Soon afterward the mother became ill. Knowing that death was near, she called the child to her bedside. "I must leave you, Little Flower," she said. "But when I am gone and you are lonely, look into this mirror and you will always see me."

Many months later the father married again, but the new wife did not like the child and often spoke sharply to her. On these occasions the little girl would slip quietly into a corner of her room, unwrap the mirror from its green silk covering and gaze into it, seeming always to see her mother's face.

One day her stepmother saw her crouching over some object and whispering to it. Storming out to her husband she said, "Your daughter is performing some wicked magic. She hates me and is trying to kill me by bringing evil spirits into the house. Perhaps she has even made an image and is sticking pins into it!"

"This cannot be!" cried the father, unable to believe such things of his gentle child. Just the same, he went at once to her room. There she was in the corner, murmuring to herself and peering down at something in her hands. At the sound of his footsteps she hastily thrust the object into her long sleeve.

"My wife was right!" he exclaimed. "She has told me you are trying to injure her through evil spirits, and now I see that she is not mistaken!"

At these bitter, unjust words, the child's eyes brimmed with tears. "Your wife is dear to you; I would never want to harm her!" Then she slipped the mirror from her sleeve. "Just before my mother died she gave this to me and bade me look into it whenever I became lonely. There on its shining surface I see her kind face, and it brings peace to my aching heart."

The stepmother had crept in quietly behind her husband, and at these words she took the child in her arms. "Forgive me," she whispered. "I too will help to keep sorrow from dwelling in your heart."

Thus love came back into the house to dispel its bleak shadows. From that time on, when the child looked into the mirror, it was a smiling face that greeted her.

From very ancient times mirrors had a deep significance in Japanese life, for it was a mirror that drew the Sun Goddess from her cave and thus restored light to heaven and earth. Further, the creator god Izanagi had presented his children with a bright metal disc and bade them look into it every day. By allowing only heavenly thoughts to dwell in their minds, they would be assured that the disc would always reveal a pure heart.

chin chin kobakama

She was a pretty little wife, but oh, so lazy! Her parents had been rich, able to afford enough servants to take care of her silk kimonos, to dress her hair, and to wait on her in a dozen ways. When she grew up and married, however, there wasn't nearly enough money for a host of servants and so she had to do many things for herself. Her husband was a warrior, and as he was away for long periods of time fighting battles for the emperor, she could often be as lazy as she pleased without his even knowing about it. But she was so pretty that he probably wouldn't have minded anyhow.

One night when her husband was away, she was awakened by strange noises. She lit her lantern. There upon her pillow were scores of queer little men about one inch tall. They were dressed in armor, wore their hair in topknots, and had tiny swords at their belts. Thus they looked for all the world just like her husband when he was setting out for the wars. Around her pillow they danced at a dizzy pace and then began to sing:

Chin Chin Kobakama,
We are the Chin Chin Kobakama;
The hour is late—
Sleep, honorable, noble darling.

Now these words seemed harmless enough, but it didn't take the young wife long to realize that the little men were really making fun of her, especially as they made faces every time she looked them squarely in the eye.

At first it was rather fun to watch these miniature warriors, but after a while she became sleepy and wished they would go away. She asked them to leave, quite politely, but they paid no attention. All night long they sang and danced on her pillow, until she was very tired of it all.

She hoped that they too were worn out and would never come back. The next night, though, just at the hour of the ox, which is two o'clock in the morning, there they were again. This time she was frightened and tried to drive them away. But they were much too nimble and quick, slipping through her fingers and bobbing up again in every direction. There were hundreds of them now, and her pretty head began to spin just as wildly as the wee men did.

In the days and weeks that followed, she became ill through fright and lack of sleep, for the tiny warriors would not leave her alone for a single night. When her husband returned, he was alarmed by her pale, drawn face. With a bit of coaxing he managed to get the whole story from her.

"Tonight I will hide in your closet with the door slightly open," he decided. "Then we'll see what these pesky intruders are up to."

Promptly at the hour of the ox the diminutive warriors came as usual. The husband almost laughed aloud at the sight of

their wee daggers and their hair tied up in knots just like his. Then he heard his wife's frightened moans and became angry instead.

He decided at once that they must be either goblins, ghosts, or fairies—and all these creatures are afraid of swords. Out he jumped from his hiding place, brandishing his weapon. In an instant the tiny men turned into—toothpicks! No more dancing, fierce little warriors—just a heap of toothpicks!

Being very polite he turned his head away so that he wouldn't embarrass his wife by seeing her blushes. They both knew what had happened. She had been too lazy to put her toothpicks away regularly; it had been easier just to tuck them down between the thick mats of woven reeds that covered the floor. The fairies who take care of the mats insist that they be kept clean because the Japanese eat, sleep, and sit on the floor rather than on furniture. Becoming incensed with this little wife who was careless with her floor mats, the fairies had taken the shape of tiny warriors to torment her.

But they never had to come back, for the very sight of a toothpick from that time on sent her scurrying about the house to make sure that every inch was clean.

A Japanese room is measured by the number of mats it contains; thus there is a four-mat room, a six-mat room, an eight-mat room, etc. The largest rooms contain one hundred mats fitted closely together edge to edge. As the Japanese never wear shoes in the house and the mats are usually replaced once a year, the floor is always clean.

More examples of Japanese names for hours:

Hour of the dragon	8 a.m.
" " " hare	6 a.m.
" " " tiger	4 a.m.
" " " rat	12 midnight
" " " monkey	4 p.m.
" " " snake	10 a.m.
" " " horse	11 a.m.

the sennin

Kumeno was a Sennin, one of those mystic hermits who live among the pine trees of lofty mountain tops where they achieve so perfect an understanding of nature that they are no longer like ordinary men. Not only are they immortal, but they can perform all kinds of magical feats such as walking on water, flying like birds, ejecting their own images through their mouths, and summoning animals out of the air.

It was not easy to attain these mystic powers. Only through rigid self-discipline and denial of many pleasures did they come. One of Kumeno's fellow Sennin kept cutting down his meals until at last he lived on one grain of millet a day. Another stood in icy water for hours every night, gladly enduring physical discomfort so that his spirit might soar. Few took shelter even in bitter weather. The ground was their bed and the mountain air their coverlet.

An ever-present danger lurked behind every Sennin: if even for an instant he yielded to earthly desires he would lose all the supernatural abilities he had struggled so hard to attain.

Now Kumeno's particular joy was flying. Nothing was more exhilarating than to soar through the skies, dipping close to earth when he pleased or gliding up through the clouds on days when they looked particularly fresh. Life had become even less complicated for him than for the Sennin who ate only a grain of millet a day, for Kumeno had trained himself to live on air alone.

One day he was floating over a valley beribboned with crystal streams when he was attracted by two objects gleaming white in the waters below. He came down for a closer look and discovered that they were the feet of a young girl washing clothes in the river. Descending a bit lower, he saw that the rest of the maiden was as fair as the feet.

It was a critical moment. Kumeno knew very well how dangerous it was to become interested in earthly things. He looked again at the girl. Yes, she was very pretty indeed. Then he glanced upward to the clouds. A bit stuffy they seemed. Momentarily he poised in mid-air, one foot toeing upward, the other down. But he had lingered too long. His supernatural power began to slip away. One instant he was as buoyant as a dragonfly; the next, he was plummeting like a rock.

He landed unharmed on a mossy knoll not far from the surprised maiden who was responsible for his downfall. But now he was just like any man, all his magical arts gone forever. No more flying through the heavens or strolling on the waters. He was like ordinary men in another way, too: the girl still looked better to him than the clouds did.

And thus all was not lost, for Kumeno married the maiden with the white feet and they probably lived happily ever after.

Icarus of Greek mythology could fly also. He came to grief because he soared too high, Kumeno because he dipped too low.

Sennin occur frequently both in the legends and arts of Japan. Some of them have become especially famous because they are identified with a group of immortals known as the "Seven Deities of Good Luck," a rollicking crew who come to port on a Treasure Ship each New Year's eve. Their cargo includes such magical items as a Hat of Invisibility and an Inexhaustible Purse. Children place pictures of the Treasure Ship under their pillows during the New Year festival to bring lucky dreams.

Uzume, the merry little goddess who danced before the cave of the Sun Goddess Amaterasu, is sometimes shown as a companion of the Seven Deities of Good Luck.

the jellyfish and the monkey

The Sea God was most unhappy. He had recently married a Dragon Princess, but she had become ill and nothing in all the four seas could tempt her appetite or make her well. Anxiously he hovered over her for days. Then one morning she sighed, "If I could only have the liver of a live monkey, I'm sure I would recover at once."

The Sea God sent immediately for his most trusted retainer, the jellyfish. "Go to land and bring back a live monkey," said the god. "This is just the task for you, because you have legs and thus can walk on the shore. And do hurry!"

Well, clearly jellyfish were different in those days from what they are now!

The jellyfish bowed low. How gratifying to be entrusted with so important a task!

Up through the waters he swam until he came to a wooded shore. There, sporting among the trees, was a monkey. The jellyfish settled himself under a pine and, after a respectable silence, murmured, "How dull life must be for you!"

"Dull!" said the monkey, a bit affronted. "No one has so much fun as I."

"I pity you, my friend," continued the jellyfish. "Never have you seen anything but these drab woods. As for me, I come from a land where coral palaces are lined with pearl and diamonds drip like dewdrops from the trees. And the food! Delicacies like those, I cannot even describe!"

The monkey came closer. Coral palaces sounded rather chilly, but food never failed to interest him, though at the moment his appetite was a bit jaded.

"Are visitors allowed in the Dragon Kingdom?" he hinted.

"Oh my yes," said the jellyfish. "The Sea King is an admirable host. If you'd like to come for a holiday, just hop on my back and I'll be glad to take you."

The monkey accepted the invitation at once, and the jellyfish could hardly refrain from chuckling aloud as he watched the agile little fellow make hurried preparations for the journey. These land creatures were such innocents!

But halfway down to the Dragon Kingdom a disturbing thought struck the jellyfish. "By the way," he said, "you do have your liver along, don't you?"

"My liver!" said the monkey. "How personal you fish are! Whatever makes you ask?"

"Well, you see our Dragon Queen is ill and needs the liver of a live monkey."

"Dear me, what a pity! Why didn't you tell me? I have several livers, but I left them all hanging on a branch in my back yard."

The jellyfish was crushed. "However," said the monkey helpfully, "if you'll take me home again I'll be glad to get one for you."

Back they went. The monkey scurried to the top of the tallest tree and began to pelt the jellyfish with nuts. "Go back to your coral palaces," he taunted, "and next time your king sends you on an errand, bring your wits as well as your body. In the meantime, I shall continue to take my liver with me wherever I go."

When the jellyfish reported back to his master, the Sea God was furious and he ordered his attendants to give the retainer a sound thrashing. They did such a thorough job of it that his shell and bones became soft as jelly, and he and his descendants have been in that condition ever since.

As for the Dragon Queen, she was so amused by the whole situation that she recovered immediately, even without the liver of a live monkey.

Japan has numerous stories of monkeys, perhaps because they are one of its few wild animals. Many are caught and tamed. Troupes of monkeys used to give theatrical performances throughout the country. They were trained to handle swords, to cry like women, and to use dogs as horses.

On the guide-stones at crossroads in Japan one often sees a picture of the Deity of the Roads. Beside him are his attendants, three mystic monkeys. The first one covers his ears with his hands that he may hear no evil, the second his eyes that he may see no evil, and the third his mouth that he may speak no evil. The three monkeys are also seen in a famous carved panel above the royal stable at Nikko where a sacred white horse is kept for the use of the gods.

A real monkey is maintained in the stables of the imperial palace to entertain the horses. The two animals are closely associated in Japanese legend, and an old proverb says "The heart is like the monkey whereas the head is like the horse."

Associated with the immortals of Greek myth is a famous white horse too—the winged Pegasus (peg' ah suss), steed of the Nine Muses.

Buddha and the Whale

"It's the biggest thing in Japan!"

"Fifty feet high, they say, even though it is in a sitting position!"

"Its eyelids alone must be four feet long. And those thumbs—at least three feet around!"

"Look at the eyes; they're of pure gold."

Day after day admiring pilgrims from all over Japan had been coming to the city of Kamakura to admire the great bronze statue of Buddha which had just been completed. In a magnificent temple it sat, hands folded and an expression of profound peace on its great face.

Among the onlookers was a group of sailors, and even after they had gone back to their ships and sailed far into the northern seas, they were still talking about the Great Buddha at Kamakura. Now the whale just happened to be passing by as one sailor said, "Without a doubt it is the most colossal thing in the world." The whale nearly turned a handspring. What! Something bigger than he? Ridiculous! Sailors just couldn't be depended upon to tell a story without exaggeration. With a snort that nearly upset the boat, and sent the sailors scuttling to their storm stations, the whale flicked his tail in derision and swam away.

But he was worried. The story was a foolish rumor, of course, but he didn't even like rumors that made him smaller than something else. At first he brooded about it only at bedtime; after a while it began to haunt him three times a day; at last his worry developed into a full-time occupation. He lost weight and became quite pale.

An amiable old shark noticed the anxious frown that cut across the whale's forehead like a newly dredged canal, and one day he ventured to ask, "What is it that bothers you, my friend? Never have I seen you look so doleful."

Now ordinarily the whale would have considered this an impertinence, but now that his whole life had become topsy-turvy, he wanted nothing so much as to talk over his problem with someone. Soon he had blubbered out the whole story. The shark listened respectfully and then puckered his brow in thought. Here was a proud moment; what is more satisfying than to give sage advice to one's superiors?

"I have it!" he said at last. "You look much too weak for any journey at this moment, but I will go to Kamakura and measure the statue for you. Then at least you will know whether to start eating again or to commit suicide."

Gratefully the whale accepted the generous offer, and the shark swished down south to Kamakura. When he came to a spot on the shore where he could see the image towering above him about a half mile inland, he was first elated and then confused. He really hadn't thought this through very carefully; never having learned how to walk on his tail or his fins, how was he to travel by land?

Too bad, he thought, and was just about to go back when he caught sight of a sprightly rat enjoying a moonlight scamper on the decks of a nearby boat. Now here was someone with the proper equipment. Coming alongside the craft, he told the rat of the whale's problem and asked for suggestions. Enormously flattered, the rat came up with an answer at once. He himself would undertake the great mission; he personally would measure the Buddha.

He swam ashore and scurried to the temple. But he had no measuring stick. Back he went to the shark. "I have nothing to measure with," he protested.

"Walk around the statue and count your steps," said the shark, who always prided himself on having quick answers.

Again the rat went to the statue and, starting at a point roughly parallel with the Buddha's left elbow, he paced around the huge figure, counting his footsteps aloud so that he wouldn't lose track. "Four thousand and ninety-eight, four thousand and ninety-nine, five thousand." How pleasant to have it come out in a nice round number like that; it added dignity somehow.

When the shark heard the news, his jaw dropped in amazement and both rows of teeth gleamed so pearly white in the moonlight that the rat was temporarily lost in admiration. "This will be a blow to the whale," said the shark gravely. "I doubt if even he is that big around. However, I must be on my way to deliver the sad message. Thank you, my friend."

When the whale learned that his rival was five thousand rat-feet in circumference, he leaped so high into the air that he caused a tidal wave. "I don't believe it! I'll never believe it! I shall uncover the facts for myself and stop these reckless rumors once and for all!" Then he just happened to remember that he had a pair of magic boots that would enable him to travel as well on land as on sea. Tucking them under his left-front fin, he charged southward.

He made excellent time because he looked so fierce that the traffic melted away before him. But even so it was dark when he reached Kamakura, and the priests had all gone to bed. Never mind. This pesky business had to be taken care of immediately, for the nervous strain was more than he could bear. Going up to the temple, he knocked. From within came the deep, bronze voice of the statue. "Come in."

"I can't," said the whale. "I'm much too big." Just saying the word "big" made him feel better right away.

"Then I shall come out," said the statue.

Rising from his pedestal, he went through the temple gates into the night. When he saw the whale he nearly toppled over in astonishment. After staring down at all those lilliputian priests

and pilgrims, the statue found this enormous creature quite a shock. The whale, for his part, was so frightened that his fins knocked. But gradually he recovered his composure and stated his mission. The statue was most understanding; besides, he was a bit curious himself to see who was the bigger.

In the meantime the priests had been awakened by strange noises that sounded like a conversation between a bronze bell and a storm at sea. Hurrying outside, they saw what appeared at first to be a rather ungainly dance by the statue and the whale. But on closer inspection they discovered that the two were just sidling around each other trying to determine which was the larger.

"Allow me to help," said the head priest. Using his rosary as a measuring tape, he methodically went around first the statue and then the whale, making careful computations each step of the way. With clenched fists and fins they watched, and the furrow on the whale's brow deepened another ten feet. At last the priest had finished. "It is my pleasure and my sorrow to announce that one of you is exactly two inches taller and wider than the other." He paused for dramatic effect. "The distinction of being the biggest thing in the world goes to…the whale!"

Dizzy with relief, the whale reeled back to the northern waters and the statue returned to his pedestal and sat down. He was a stoical soul, for his face to this day is as serene as if he had never heard of a whale or discovered that there is something in the world bigger than he.

The Daibutsu, which means "Great Buddha," of Kamakura is one of the most remarkable sights in Japan and the most famous statue of Buddha in the world. It was made in the Thirteenth Century of bronze sheets that were shaped and finished by chisels. The great hall in which it originally stood was washed away by a tidal wave in 1465, and since then it has towered unsheltered above the trees.

PART THREE

WHITE BANNERS
of the minamoto

One of the most popular of Japan's many festivals is Boys' 161
Day, celebrated on May 5. Flags swirl in the breeze and roofs
of houses are decorated with iris leaves. Every family with sons
puts up a tall pole in the garden and from it flies a kite shaped
like the carp—a fish that swims against the current—for each boy.
The eldest son gets the largest, the baby the smallest. As the
wind catches these paper fish they seem to be battling their way
through the air—an example to Japanese boys to be strong and
brave enough to fight against all adversity.

Inside the house, shelves are set up to display tiny figures
fashioned and dressed to represent the country's greatest warriors
and heroes. These dolls, which are handed down from generation to generation, are in armor and carry weapons.

One figure is always there—a young warrior whose face and
pose clearly depict the nobility and courage that the Japanese
cherish. Yet at the same time he is both elegant and gentle. This
is Yoshisune, the ideal type of attractive character in Japan and
probably its most popular hero.

Also prominent in the display is the figure of a huge, bewhis-
kered warrior-priest, an interesting contrast to the dashing Yoshi-

sune. This is Benkei, Priest of the Western Pagoda, who could vanquish one hundred swordsmen at once.

Yoshisune and Benkei lived in the Twelfth Century when two clans, the Minamoto and Taira, struggled for mastery. Four hundred years earlier, Kyoto had become the seat of the emperor's court and thus the capital of Japan. The city nestled between high mountains whose thickly wooded slopes were studded with innumerable temples and shrines. Magnificent gates, bridges, and palaces adorned the city, and beyond was a scenic countryside where aristocrats went for moon-viewing parties or for the highly popular horse races.

Supposedly the emperor was still supreme ruler of Japan. But the real power had passed into the hands of the Fujiwara family, who filled all important government posts and contrived to have the emperor and the princes marry only Fujiwara daughters.

Under the rule of this luxury-loving family, Japan entered into a golden age of art, music, and literature. Japan's first real novel, *The Tale of Genji,* by Lady Murasaki, was written during this period. Splendid performances of song and dance—the early beginnings of the No drama—developed. Playing musical instruments and writing tanka became an important part of daily life. One man, Sugawara Mechizane, so endeared himself as a patron of literature that he was worshipped after his death as the God of Letters. In his honor Japanese children still enjoy a special school holiday.

The nobles lived in elegance, both men and women wearing rainbow-hued silks, decorating their faces with cosmetics, dyeing their teeth black, and perfecting the art of blending perfumes.

But by the beginning of the Twelfth Century, discontent and crime were rife throughout Japan because the Fujiwara had become more interested in sumptuous living and courtly manners than in good government. Hordes of people lived in wretched poverty. Travel was perilous. Powerful militaristic families warred against each other, ruthlessly burning villages of peasants and trampling their fields in the process. Even many of the monks and priests had learned to fight, and there were armed clashes between great temples and monasteries.

Unable to quell the ever-mounting disorder, the Fujiwara family was eventually forced to relinquish its power to the Heike, or Taira clan, under the leadership of the chieftain Kiyomori. But in time the Taira also succumbed to the splendor of courtly life in Kyoto and governed no better than their predecessors. Then rebellion flared more hotly than ever, for in their attempt to maintain control the new rulers became cruel and tyrannical.

A rival clan, the Genji or Minamoto, then challenged the power of the Taira. But Kiyomori treacherously murdered the Minamoto leader Yoshidomo, whose young wife had to flee on foot through the winter snows with her baby in her arms and two small sons hanging on to her skirts.

That baby was Yoshisune. His exploits, triumphs, and defeats have fascinated the Japanese people down through the centuries. Poets told the Yoshisune story in literary masterpieces such as the *Heike Monogatari*, which means *Tale of the Heike*. Ballad singers chanted it on street corners to the accompaniment of the four-stringed biwa. Artists put it into their paintings, prints, and sculptures. Playwrights wove it into the classical No dramas and other plays. For more than seven hundred years Japanese children have heard the tales in school and read them in their favorite books.

Even in games the heroes of that struggle between the Heike and Genji are immortalized. The faces of the two favorites, Yoshisune and Benkei, are frequently seen on the huge kites—some of them six feet square—that little boys and grown men alike enjoy flying in the February and March winds. Sometimes boys name their kites Genji or Heike, and each side tries to destroy those of the other. The string for ten or twenty feet near the kite end is covered with glue and then dipped into powdered glass. By getting the kite into proper position and sawing at the string of the antagonist, a skillful boy can bring down his opponent's kite.

Another game, now forbidden by the government as too dangerous, was called "The Genji and the Heike." Boys chose up sides, the Genji wearing white flags on their backs, the Heike red ones. Each contestant had a round piece of earthenware over his head. Armed with bamboo sticks, the two sides fought to break the earthenware discs of the enemy. Often these teams consisted of several hundred boys marshaled into regular battle squadrons.

Thus does the turbulent Twelfth Century still live on in the life, art, and imagination of modern-day Japanese. At the very heart of this exciting heritage from the past are Yoshisune, boy-hero of Japan; and Benkei, Priest of the Western Pagoda. This is their story.

the tengu king

"Yoshisune! Yoshisune! Do not forget! With you lie the hopes of the Minamoto!"

Like the music of silver-toned bells the words entered the mind and heart of the sleeping boy. With gentle insistence they came again and again, and Yoshisune struggled to break through the mists of sleep that bound him. Moonlight stole through the latticed windows, and in the glow Yoshisune seemed to see his sad-faced mother. Her hands reached out to him imploringly.

"Remember, my son, remember. Your father died at the hands of the Taira."

Then at last the boy shook off the coils of sleep and sprang from his bed to clasp her in his arms. She was gone, but the room still seemed to hold her beauty and the echo of her words.

"Have no fear, my mother," he whispered. "I think of little else, day after day, but the task that lies before me."

Dressing himself and taking from its hiding place a small wooden sword, Yoshisune crept from his tiny room, through the monastery halls, and into the night. A singing joy surged into his heart as he sped down the moonlit path leading to his retreat in the valley below. Someday he would vanquish the hated Taira clan and restore the dignity of the Minamoto; someday he would avenge the death of his father Yoshidomo, so foully slain by the Taira chief Kiyomori.

He had been only a baby when his mother Tokiwa had been awakened at night by the crackle of flame and the terrified whisper of her serving maid: "My lady! The Taira! They have set the palace on fire!" Into the winter night Tokiwa had fled with her three small sons. Valiantly she had forced her way through trackless field and wood, her bruised and torn feet leaving a crimson trail of blood in the snow.

She had escaped. But the Taira had ways of bringing her back. They let it be rumored that her aged mother had been made a prisoner and would be put to death if her daughter did not return. Tokiwa had bowed her head in defeat, returned to Kyoto, and given herself up. Then, to save her children, the beautiful young mother had become the wife of her husband's slayer, Kiyomori. Though he loved the mother, he feared the children and intended to destroy them. But Tokiwa's pleas had softened his heart, and he had sent the three boys to separate monasteries to be trained as peaceful monks.

But even as Yoshisune studied the sacred books and learned to chant Buddhist prayers, his heart burned with determination to become a swordsman and leader skillful enough to expel the hated Taira from the land.

With these thoughts racing through his mind that night, the boy emerged into a small secluded ravine where sharp-toothed boulders crouched in the shadows and the occasional shrill cry of monkeys shattered the silence. To this spot Yoshisune had come night after night for many weeks to practice fencing. He had been forbidden by the monks, on Kiyomori's orders, to possess a weapon of any sort, but he had carved for himself a small wooden sword that he would thrust at rocks and trees as if they were the enemies of his father.

Suddenly as he darted among his imaginary foes, Yoshisune heard a clap of thunder so loud that the entire mountain seemed to rock. Wheeling about in alarm, he confronted a giant creature who towered above him like a fantastic bird ready to pounce. Ferocious eyes glared through the moon-silvered night, and an enormous nose jutted from a scowling face that seemed to belong neither to man nor bird and yet resembled both at once. Ebony

wings emerged through the folds of scarlet robes that enveloped the creature. On the head was a tiny gold coronet, and one sharp claw clutched a feathered fan.

A Tengu! Yoshisune knew well the terrifying stories about the bird-like beings who inhabited the peaks of lonely mountains. Often he had heard the frightened whisper: "Beware the Tengu! They are the reincarnations of the proud, arrogant dead, and their vengeful spirits are unquenchable. In the tops of giant trees they hold council. Woe to him that the Tengu choose to attack!"

For a long moment fear rushed through the boy's veins. Then he grasped his wooden sword and stood erect. He, a Minamoto, would not flinch even before the dreaded Tengu!

Seeing the sudden stiffening of the small figure, the Tengu broke into a contemptuous laugh. Then in a voice that sounded like the excited chirping of a thousand birds he demanded, "Who are you? Why do you leap about so ridiculously with that wooden toy?"

The lad stood tall. "I am Yoshisune of the Minamoto clan, and I yearn for the day when I shall overthrow the Taira. But I have only this poor thing to practice with."

The Tengu's eyes flashed, and his mighty wings began to twitch. He too hated the proud and brutal Taira! He too wished to break their haughty and arrogant spirits! Tossing aside his splendid red robes, the Tengu drew a magnificent sword from their folds.

"This is yours," he said to the startled boy, "and I, King of the Tengu, will teach you how to use it."

He clapped his hands. There was a flurry of wings, and instantly the glade was filled with twenty smaller Tengu all armed with gleaming swords. "First you shall fight with these, my subjects," said the Tengu king, "until you are skillful enough to face me alone. The least expert of them all will be your first opponent, but even he surpasses in speed and dexterity the greatest of the Japanese warriors."

At these words one of the creatures skipped forward and began to parry and thrust at Yoshisune with such ferocity that the youth fell back gasping against a rock. All the other Tengu broke into shrill laughter and began to thump their fat stomachs as if they were war drums. Recovering his balance, Yoshisune struck out gallantly against his fierce opponent. Now the air was filled with the sound of thrashing wings as the Tengu king flew back and forth above the fighters, screaming instructions to Yoshisune and darting down to help him ward off a blow whenever the smaller Tengu became too violent. Hour after hour the lessons went on, until the boy's long black hair streamed wildly in the moonlight and his breath came in tortured gasps.

"Enough!" shouted the Tengu king at last. "Be here tomorrow!" A rush of wings like a tornado twisting through a forest— and the Tengu were gone.

Every night after that, as soon as the monks were asleep, Yoshisune crept down to the glade, where the Tengu would descend upon him in a clash of thunder. Never was there a more eager pupil. Swiftly the boy learned to defend himself against one Tengu, then two and three at once. Imitating their lithe movements, he became so nimble that he could soar from rock

to rock like a bird and dart about so quickly that his opponents spun like tops trying to keep sight of him.

For three years the lessons continued, until at last he was able to fight all twenty Tengu at once. Now the king no longer instructed him but stood with folded wings, glorying in the skill of his young pupil.

Then came the night when Yoshisune was confronted, not by the twenty Tengu but by the king himself. "You are a worthy antagonist for the greatest of the Tengu. Yoshisune, prepare to defend yourself to the death!"

He, a mortal, to fight the Tengu king, the dreaded gnome of the mountains! Yoshisune quailed, but only for a moment. Already the king had tossed aside his scarlet robes, unsheathed his sword, and was swooping down on him. The youth lunged to the attack, and now the swords of master and pupil clashed with a violence that seemed to rip the glade with lightning bolts. Yoshisune used all the tricks he had been taught and in desperation conjured up new ones that made the giant Tengu's glaring eyes smolder with admiration.

The twenty smaller Tengu, wild with excitement at first, quickly lapsed into nervous twitterings and then into awed silence. Never among men or gnomes had there been so tempestuous and wild a battle. For hours the struggle continued, until at last Yoshisune whipped the sword from the Tengu's claw and pressed his own sharp blade against the bird-like throat.

"I yield!" cried the Tengu. "You are the greatest swordsman in Japan! Now go, for there is nothing more I can teach you!"

A roar of wings—and Yoshisune was alone, with nothing but an unutterable weariness and a glistening weapon to suggest that he had fought and defeated the most ferocious of all swordsmen, the King of the Tengu.

171

Japanese legend teems with stories of these winged, long-nosed creatures who hold their revels amid thunder and lightning on mountain peaks and in remote valleys. To spy on them is death, for they are swift to scent out human beings. Boulders hurtling down mountainsides, torrents inundating rice paddies—these and other misfortunes are said to be the mischief of the Tengu. Occasionally they steal and hide human beings who, if finally returned to their homes, are hopelessly insane.

Artists depict them in various ways, frequently with a long moustache and a beard descending to the feet. Almost always they carry a fan of seven feathers. Paintings and other art objects often show Yoshisune fighting the twenty small Tengu under the supervision of their king.

The tragic Tokiwa escaping through a swirling snowstorm with her three little ones is a favorite subject with Japanese writers and artists. The blood from her lacerated feet came to symbolize the red flag of the Taira, and snow the white flag of the Minamoto.

a young demon

While Yoshisune was growing up in the monastery on Mount
Kurama, learning Buddhist prayers by day and Tengu swordsmanship by night, Benkei was growing up in a tiny village not
far away.

From the beginning he had been a problem. No one had so
prodigious an appetite as Benkei. He had been born hungry and
had stayed hungry ever since. Despite the efforts of his hardworking little mother and grandfather, there was never enough
food in the flimsy wood-and-paper hut to satisfy him.

Neighbors waggled their heads disapprovingly and predicted
dire things. Had he not been born with a full set of teeth, hair
down to his shoulders, and limbs so sturdy that he could outrun
the wind? And was he not now outgrowing other boys so rapidly
that he made them look like dwarfs? Besides, he was so full of
unexpected tricks that people sidled out of the way whenever
he came in sight. "Young demon!" sniffed the neighbors. "He will
come to a bad end!"

There were other problems too. Benkei was not only the
biggest and most mischievous boy in the village but also the
laziest. He detested work and developed great talent for avoiding
it. When his grandfather asked for help in his blacksmith shop,
the boy brought down the hammer with such force that the anvil
was buried two feet in the ground and the tiny workroom almost
fell apart from the impact of the blow. When told to bring home
firewood, he uprooted a full-grown pine tree, bore it down the

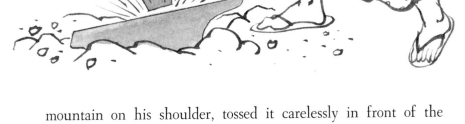

mountain on his shoulder, tossed it carelessly in front of the doorway and thus blocked the entrance.

"Cut it up!" screamed the infuriated grandfather. Benkei did —with such gusto that an avalanche of flying chips battered the walls and roof of the hut and sent mother and grandfather scurrying to the woods for safety.

They gave up after that: it was easier just to let Benkei, now a fifteen-year-old giant, wander unmolested through the hills, sniffing the balmy air and scheming how to get more food and do less work.

One day as he was roaming through the mountains, he came to a cliff on which was poised a gigantic boulder. Recent storms having partially dislodged it, the rock seemed ready to hurtle at any moment down the precipice to the temple below. An idea came to Benkei. He was hungry and the temple was in danger. Here was a situation with possibilities.

With jaunty step he swung down and approached a group of priests lounging about the gates.

"Would you like to have that boulder removed?" he asked.

The priests stared at him and then burst into laughter. "And who would move it?" asked one.

"For as much food as I can eat for as long as I want to stay here, I will," said Benkei.

The priests shrieked with delight. This boy had an imagination as huge as his body. The boulder must weigh at least a thousand pounds. But why not go along with the joke?

"We accept the bargain!" one of them cried. "Ya-a! Ya-a!" assented the others.

Benkei scowled. He didn't like being laughed at. Stalking up to the precipice, he began to tug at the boulder but could get no grip on it. Undaunted, he put his back to the rock. Then the chuckling priests saw the muscles of his legs, shoulders, and neck begin to bulge like twisted ropes.

"He's moving it!" someone squealed, and the laughter faded into shocked gasps.

Slowly Benkei worked the boulder up to his back, to his neck, and with a final shove, onto his two hands. Then holding it high above his head, he called down to the gaping priests, "Do I still get all I can eat, or shall I dump this piece of mountain on your temple?"

The rock teetered a bit on the giant hands. "All you can eat! All you can eat!" babbled those of the priests who still had their breath and their wits.

"Where shall I put it?" called Benkei.

Speechless now, the head priest pointed to a terrace a hundred feet away. With the rock still held above his head, Benkei carried it to the designated spot and heaved it down the mountain.

Now for the first time in his life Benkei had enough to eat—and eat he did. The priests watched first in fascination and then in horror as the young giant ate his way through supplies that were to last the temple for months. Sometimes when his appetite was especially good he devoured all the food prepared for the entire monastery, and the priests clutched their stomachs helplessly and went to bed hungry. He seemed to grow before their

very eyes, or was it just that *they* were shrinking into shadows of their former robust selves?

The temple was on the verge of ruin. Something had to be done. Down to the city scurried the head priest to the home of a wealthy merchant. "This giant can do the work of fifty men," he urged. "What an asset for a clever business man like you!"

So Benkei, lured from the temple by promises of even more food in the home of the merchant, went down to the city. The first day he loaded rice carts so fast that he kept all the other workers racing just to haul the filled vehicles away and to put new ones in place. A week's work completed in two hours! The merchant rejoiced and dreamed that night of heaps of gold springing up like bean sprouts all over his warehouses. A few days later Benkei had become bored. Time for strategy again. Suddenly the startled workmen found that their huge companion was tossing the bags far beyond the carts into the fields. Protests brought only an amused grin. Benkei's career as a merchant's helper was at an end.

ohaya and the golden carp

Above the city of Kyoto was Mount Hiei in whose wooded ravines more than a thousand temples and monasteries were cradled. What better life, thought Benkei as he turned his broad back forever on such tedious things as merchants and rice bales and work, than that of a monk: lots of food, freedom to roam through the mountains, and—most important of all—a chance to learn swordsmanship and the use of bow and arrow. For the priests of Mount Hiei were the most warlike in all Japan. They felt that they were mistreated by the Taira rulers, and from time to time they swarmed down from the mountain, storming the capital and flourishing their weapons by way of demanding their rights. Between skirmishes they spent many hours learning how to use the sword and lance more effectively for the next encounter.

Benkei enrolled as a student in the Temple of the Western Pagoda on Mount Hiei and there behaved himself—for a while. Dutifully he learned to chant the Buddhist prayers, delighting in the sound of his sonorous voice as it boomed majestically through the temple to rival the deep melody of the monastery bells. In the use of the glaive, a sharp blade on the end of a long rod, he became a champion. Nor could any other priest wield the sword so swiftly as he.

The fame of the young giant of Mount Hiei—so strong of arm and rich of voice—spread, and people began to speak of him as the Black Priest of the Western Pagoda. For now Benkei had reached young manhood, and a determined-looking black beard bristled from cheek and chin. When he was in a jovial mood, the whiskers gave him a slightly surprised appearance; but when he was angry, his black eyes and beard seemed to sputter and sizzle like a smoke-filled volcano on the verge of erupting.

Several months after coming to the monastery, Benkei received word that his grandfather had died. The priests granted him permission to bring his mother Ohaya to live with him in a small hut outside the temple walls. It was a proud little mother who trudged up the mountain to join her warrior-priest son, her days of toil over at last.

Benkei spent his days studying, praying, fighting, and eating in the monastery while Ohaya puttered around the hut or roamed the hills in search of wild berries. But one night when he came home, Ohaya was gone. He set out to find her, but there was no answer to his shouts. In the morning he resumed his search; again he returned alone to the hut.

On the third day he traveled far from the monastery to a cedar-fringed glade into which the priests never ventured because it was said to be haunted. Wild monkeys chattered in excitement and swung low to peer into the face of this invader of their woodland home. Then several of them bustled around, scuttling back and forth into the recesses of the glade as if inviting him to follow. Catching a gleam of some gold object a short distance ahead, he trailed after the monkeys until he came to a torrential stream. In the current lay a carp so immense that it stretched from bank to bank and formed a barrier that flung the crashing waters into the air like geysers. The huge body glinted with golden scales as large as plates, and the bulbous eyes seemed to be rimmed with flame.

Benkei leaped into the water and grasped two flaring fins. In a twinkling the carp coiled itself into an arc and then straightened like a whiplash, hammering the giant with its tail. The first blow would have killed an ordinary man, but Benkei stood like a rock, taking the fearful beating while groping for a place to grasp the slippery monster more securely. At last he managed to plunge his hands deep into the quivering gills. Now the fish seemed to go wild. In a frenzy it tried to surmount the falls in one flying leap after another, and Benkei was hurled against jagged stones that tore at his flesh. Yet his fingers dug ever deeper into the creature's gills. Then the fish plummeted into the depths of a swirling, cavernous pool, but the giant's iron-muscled legs brought fish and man rocketing to the surface again. He found a foothold at last and, bracing himself against a boulder, flung the carp to the bank.

His knife slashed into the gigantic body, and in the stomach he found bits of his mother's dress. Benkei fell to his knees and wept. After a few moments he rose. "She shall be placed with her ancestors!" he shouted fiercely.

Shouldering the huge fish, Benkei carried it down the mountain to the village where he and his mother had been born. Here, after proper funeral ceremonies, he reverently entombed the golden-scaled carcass. Ohaya must be buried so that she could be worshipped with her ancestors. Since she was in the fish, what else was there to do but bury the fish?

Thus did the Black Priest of the Western Pagoda pay final respects to his mother.

Japan has many a picturesque pagoda, or tower of Buddhism, such as the one where Benkei became a priest. The first pagoda was built in the sixth century for the worship of Buddha's ashes. Later ones were erected chiefly as memorial towers in which to offer prayers for the peaceful repose of souls in the underworld. A pagoda is ordinarily octagonal in shape and may have from one to thirteen stories—always an odd number, for odd numbers suggest heaven. The five-story pagoda represents the five elements of ground, water, fire, wind, and sky.

a Giant Joke

"He eats more than all the rest of us put together!"
"The best part of every meal always goes to him!"
"His silly pranks are unendurable!"
"Something must be done about Benkei!"

Glumly the priests recited their grievances. But what does one do about a powerful eight-foot giant who at the slightest provocation can become as savage as a wild boar?

For Benkei, after the death of his mother, had reverted to the old behavior that once had filled his timid little grandfather with impotent rage. No monk was safe from his annoying tricks; no monastery too private for him to honor with his unwelcome visits; no morsel on the table beyond reach of his grasping fingers.

The old wanderlust coming upon him again, Benkei had left the pagoda on Mount Hiei and had been tramping through the woods and hills in another part of the country for several months. Finding a comfortable old monastery deep in a secluded grove, he had announced himself as a fellow priest who intended to stay for a short rest.

Grudgingly the monks had consented, and at that moment their lives had undergone a sharp reorganization. There was a sudden food shortage; priestly robes developed a strange propensity to tangle into knots; sedate old monks who hadn't smiled in years quite unaccountably found themselves in absurd situations. Nerves became ragged and tempers flared. Even the temple bells began to sound irritable.

But how to get rid of Benkei!

The chance seemed to come one day when the husky young priest Kaiyen and a companion discovered the giant asleep in the woods. His snores had set every leaf to quivering.

"Such a loafer!" snorted Kaiyen, who had become progressively less husky each day since Benkei's arrival.

"And such a ridiculous-looking one," added the other as he watched the ebb and flow of the wiry whiskers.

A gleam came into Kaiyen's eyes. "I'll fix this impudent fellow so that he'll go away and never come back." From his pocket he took inkstone and brush and with infinite care sketched a silly word on each of the sleeping giant's bulging cheeks.

An hour later when Benkei strode into the dining hall, full of good humor and appetite, he was greeted with suppressed laughter. Unsuspecting he joined in, at which the mirth bubbled into a riotous chorus. Even the rector's stern face softened into a grin. For the first time in his life Benkei was embarrassed. They were laughing at him! But why?

He turned to go, and the monks howled with merriment. Passing by the refectory where a priest was delivering a sermon, he watched every face suddenly crinkle into a smile and heard muffled titters ripple through the room. Raging now, he went outside. Just beyond the temple gate he came upon a band of children who squealed with delight and imitated the antics of a monkey.

With a roar of frustration and anger, Benkei stamped over to the six-foot cistern and looked at his reflection in the water. So that was it! They had dared!

Back he thundered. Not bothering to go through the door, he vaulted over the wall and dropped into the midst of the chuckling priests. Hands on hips he roared: "Someone was bold enough to laugh *at* me. Now is he bold enough to laugh *with* me, or is he a coward?"

The laughter died a sudden death, and for a moment the monks stared spellbound at the glowering figure. Then Kaiyen

came forward. Confident of the support and sympathy of the watching monks who had applauded his little joke so enthusiastically, he said, "Yes, you dirty creature. We're sick of your rudeness, arrogance, and greed!"

Benkei gave one incredulous bellow and charged. Like frightened squirrels the monks scattered before him, tumbling over each other in panic. Kaiyen wavered for a moment and then, seeing his supporters desert him, fled. Through the halls and yard he ran, the giant pounding at his heels. The other monks gathered in terrified little groups at a safe distance and began to chant prayers for their unfortunate brother.

Cornered at last in the kitchen, Kaiyen snatched a burning log from the fire and swung it. Benkei dodged the blow and then, as effortlessly as a mother cat picks up her kitten, plucked the fellow up by neck and thigh and tossed him to the roof.

"You want him back?" he said to the priests. "Go get him!" Picking up his staff, Benkei marched down the mountain.

But as he turned into the highway leading toward Mount Hiei, he heard the clang of temple bells. Looking back he saw smoke and flame billowing from the monastery he had just left. At once he guessed what had happened. The burning log had also flown through the air when Kaiyen so unceremoniously sailed up to the roof. The glowing embers had ignited the thatch, and flames had leaped from one wooden building to another.

"Too bad, too bad," muttered Benkei, remembering with regret the temple's satiny panelings, rich ornaments, and elaborate carvings. "Now to get it rebuilt..."

He was certain that a messenger would be dispatched immediately to the capital to inform the emperor. But Benkei knew that with his knowledge of every shortcut through the mountains he could easily get there first. Abruptly he left the highway and turned to the foothills, a plan beginning to squirm around in his mind.

The next evening as the young emperor and his courtiers were enjoying the summer breeze in the garden, a voice—deep, sonorous, musical as a great bronze bell—floated down from the peaks above the city. "The temple! The temple! The Harima temple has been burned! It must be rebuilt at once! See to it, O Emperor! Do not delay!"

Three times the voice pealed forth its message, and the echoes soared from cliff to cliff until the entire mountain seemed to be intoning the command.

The young emperor summoned his court diviner. "What does this mean?"

The old man looked in his ancient books and then said solemnly, "This is a warning of a Tengu from yonder peaks. You dare not ignore it, Your Majesty. The temple must be rebuilt at once."

From a lofty perch on the bluff, Benkei watched with amused satisfaction the glowing lanterns and bustling excitement below. Then he saw a little procession trail out from the capital. Tossing aside the roll of paper that he had twisted into a trumpet, he started down the mountain. The temple would be rebuilt—and quickly.

one thousand swords

"Can you make a sword worthy of a hand and an arm this size?"

The busy little swordmaker glanced up casually from his work and then jerked to full attention. Towering in his doorway and filling it almost to the last crevice was a huge, black-robed priest whose fierce eyes darted sharply and impatiently around the shop.

"F-f-for you?" stuttered the nervous little artisan.

"For me," repeated Benkei, "and it must be the best sword you have ever made."

"B-but it would take a thousand ordinary swords to make one fit for you because I could use only the points and edges."

"A thousand! Nothing easier," said Benkei. "I'll be back."

Striding out into the sunshine, Benkei chuckled. This would be fun. That very night he would start his collection. Thousand was a magic number. Hidehira had a thousand horses, Tametsugu had a thousand suits of armor, Benkei would collect a thousand swords and be as famous as anybody. Nothing but the best for Benkei.

That evening five young warriors walking along the highway leading into Kyoto suddenly found their path barred by a giant priest.

"Your swords, please. Will you give them or shall I take them?"

"Why, the infernal impudence...!" The sentence was never finished, for the next moment the warrior found himself flying through the air like a kite in a high wind. When the mists cleared before his eyes, he saw that he was not alone: his four companions lay in confused heaps by his side, and there was not a sword among them.

From that night on Benkei became the terror of Kyoto. Spruce young noblemen out for an evening's adventure always found it, but not the kind they had anticipated. They started out perfumed and powdered, brocade robes rustling pleasantly; they returned wild-eyed and swordless. Even the bravest warriors and most skilled swordsmen could make no stand against the huge priest who seemed to lurk in every shadow. The less valiant didn't even try: they simply threw down their weapons and ran.

Underneath the floor of his hut on Mount Hiei, Benkei dug a deep hole to accommodate an ever-growing pile of swords. His collection was coming along very well indeed.

But gradually the harvest of blades began to diminish, for men no longer dared stir from their homes after dark. The once-gay city became strangely quiet, and sometimes Benkei wandered through the streets all night long without encountering a single victim.

"Something must be done about this," grumbled Benkei. And something *was* done. For the magistrates, determined to catch the rascally priest who was disrupting the whole way of life in Kyoto, divided the city into ten districts, each to be patrolled by fifty stalwart guards. Now Benkei was happy again. Here were antagonists enough for even his stout arm. Each night he singled out a district patrol for special attention, and frequently he marched home in the early dawn with fifty swords instead of the paltry ten or fifteen of those earlier nights before the magistrates had become so helpful.

As the pile of weapons under the hut on Mount Hiei grew, so did the stories. "It isn't a man—it's a demon!"

"Only the King of the Tengu could fight like that."

"Did you see his glaring eyes?"

"His black robe hides the Tengu wings, but they are there, you may be sure."

"I intended to fight him to the end, but my blade flew out of my hand into his before I even came close."

"He never takes anything but swords. No doubt he is collecting them for the use of the Tengu henchmen whom he instructs in fencing."

Day by day the stories multiplied, and a certain little sword-maker grew hollow-eyed and pale in direct proportion to their vividness and magnitude. He could have told a tale...!

When the rumors about the Tengu king reached Benkei's ears, he was enchanted. Why hadn't he thought of this himself! Promptly he added a new act to his nightly drama. Now as he approached his victims he would roar, "I am the Tengu king of whom men speak! Fling down your weapon, or I shall kill you first and eat you afterward!" No one argued. Benkei had not a fight but a walk, for the more vigorous warriors were able to throw their swords a considerable distance in order to gain a good start just in case the Tengu decided to get both a sword and a dinner out of the encounter.

But there was one man who scoffed at these tales of a Tengu king. He was Hisatada, fencing master to 130 of Kyoto's young noblemen. His skill in the use of all weapons had made him famous throughout Japan.

"Tengu king indeed!" he snorted one night when a group of his pupils launched into the favorite topic of conversation. "He is nothing but a robber priest who has yet to meet a man really skilled in arms. I hear that he prowls on Gojo Bridge just before the hour of the ox. Tonight I shall either kill him or bring him back alive."

Cheering lustily, the pupils crowded around their master to assist him in dressing for the fight. First he donned a suit of plate armor sewed with heavy scarlet cording. Next came a helmet decorated with gold and, for added strength, sharp steel points—all handsomely topped with two plumes of heron's feathers. From the rim of the helmet projected two horns, enough in themselves to discourage even the bravest opponent. Neck and face were protected by small metal plates sewed on leather. Thigh pieces and greaves made of smaller curved plates, together with green lacquered trimmings and a blade fashioned by the most famous swordmaker in Japan, completed Hisatada's costume.

"Wait for me here," he told his admiring students. "I shall soon be back with this brash fellow who dares to call himself the Tengu king!" Grasping a lantern, Hisatada strode into the night.

Benkei, lounging against the rail of Gojo Bridge, was bored. Business had been exceedingly slow for weeks. People just didn't seem to care for evening strolls through the dark, cool streets of Kyoto any more. Such a pity, and just when he was so close to achieving his goal of a thousand swords!

Suddenly Benkei became alert. Someone was approaching. He would get one sword after all. Ah, and this would be an especially fine one too, for the stranger was dressed in magnificent armor—quite superior to any that Benkei had ever seen before—and would undoubtedly have a good weapon. A nice prize tonight!

Stepping out to the center of the bridge, Benkei opened his mouth to shatter the stillness with the usual demand. Then he heard his own words come mockingly from the stranger's mouth: "I am the Tengu. Yes, I am the Ten..."

When Hisatada regained consciousness, he was flat on his back. He had the dreamy feeling that his sword and the hand with which he had grasped it had just sailed up to the moon. No, both hands and feet were still intact, but how futilely they seemed to be waving in the air! That weight on his chest—had a log fallen on him?

Then Hisatada felt his helmet being ripped off. Greaves, armlets, and armor followed. "Stand up," ordered Benkei. "Take off the rest."

"Everything?" quavered Hisatada.

"Everything."

Back at the fencing school the students were in a fever of excitement. No one could out-fight their master; at that very moment he was probably dragging his prisoner home.

The sound of pattering feet reached their ears, and they bounded to the door. In shot a naked, shivering figure. Their master! Their skillful, fearless master, best fencer in Japan!

Hisatada glared around the room. "Yes," he said, "I have seen the Tengu king."

The Japanese have many "1,000" stories, such as those concerning the 1,000-handed Kwannon, 1,000 shrine cards, and Benkei's 1,000 swords. There are also many "imperfect 999" stories. A hunter of ancient Japan abandoned hunting when he had killed 999 boar or deer, believing that the thousandth would bring bad luck.

When painters, sculptors, and artisans such as swordmakers of ancient Japan started an unusually important job, they engaged in sakai, a ceremony of purification designed to invoke the aid of a patron deity. Before an altar erected in the workshop the artist pledged his sincerity and devotion each morning. One swordmaker who was commissioned to make a weapon for the emperor built an altar to the god Inari and underwent purification. When the sword was finished, the words "young fox" appeared on the blade. Then the swordmaker knew that his patron deity had helped him, for the fox is the messenger of Inari. Some swordmakers also underwent long fasts before making an especially important sword, one of them fasting for a hundred days before tempering the blade for a great general.

a BRIDGE, a flute, and a SWORD

In the capital city people talked of nothing else but the terrifying creature who tossed warriors around like playthings and had even defeated the renowned fencing champion. Yoshisune, coming down from the monastery to pray at the Tenjin Temple in Kyoto, heard the tale. He eyes sparkled. This oversized priest who dared to call himself a Tengu needed disciplining. What more fitting than for Yoshisune, pupil of the real Tengu king and twenty Tengu henchmen, to put the ruffian in his place and rid the city of a menace? It was time to use the skills acquired in that mossy glade on Mount Kurama.

Benkei, in the meantime, was becoming annoyed. He had 999 of the 1,000 swords, but how was he to get that last one if nobody dared venture out after dark any more? But have it he must, and so he continued to roam the city, searching for luckless wanderers.

One night as he skulked in the trees at the edge of the Gojo Bridge he heard the lilting tones of a bamboo flute. Benkei's lips curled: these Kyoto samurai were far better at making music and writing poems than in handling a sword. He had not had a really good fight since destroying that last fifty-man patrol.

What a fool this stranger was to announce his coming with a flute! He surely was aware that someone lay in wait, for everyone knows that a flute can warn its player of coming events. Yet on he came, making sweet music as serenely as if he were in the reception room of a Kyoto palace. Now the click of wooden clogs echoed on the bridge. Benkei leaped into the moonlight to barricade the way. He would make short work of this foolhardy musician.

Why, it was a boy coming toward him, a mere stripling dressed in silk and wearing a soft veil about his face! But the sword at his side! Ah, there was one worthy to complete the collection. Benkei decided at once that it would be beneath his dignity to attack this youngster; better simply to take the weapon and scare him a bit.

In amusement the giant waited, expecting to see flute and blade fly into the air as the lad bolted in terror. But nothing of the sort happened. The flute player came steadily on and began to pass by.

"Hold!" roared Benkei. "You are a bold one to be out at this hour. Have you not heard of the Tengu king? I am he. Give me your sword and then I will accompany you home to see that no harm befalls you."

Yoshisune took the bamboo flute from his lips and smiled. Benkei stared. Never had he seen so handsome and delicate a youth as this. The slanted eyes were soft, the skin fair as a blossom. Long black hair was tied on top with white silk. Then the lad spoke, and his voice was like silver bells on a frosty night.

"You want my weapon? Oh, I am much too attached to it; we are constant companions. If you want it, you must take it." Then Yoshisune put the flute to his lips and resumed his saucy playing.

Benkei had never been so astonished. Then he became angry. "So! I must chastise you, must I?" He lunged, but the boy was not there! Benkei whirled in bewilderment. A laugh floated down from the top of the high gate. There sat the youth, silhouetted against a moon-gilded sky, fanning himself gracefully.

"Fool!" Benkei's eyes glinted dangerously now. "I shall slice you like a..." The last word was lost in a thunder of protesting timber as the giant sprawled face down on the bridge. Howling

with rage, he lumbered to his feet and turned just in time to receive a stunning blow across the knuckles with an iron-ribbed war fan.

"You dare!" Now Benkei's sword flailed out in every direction. But the boy who had battled twenty Tengu at once skipped from side to side just beyond the tip of the slashing blade.

"So you like fencing?" laughed Yoshisune. "Well, take this." And suddenly Benkei had the confused notion that a thousand little roosters were charging him at once—above and below, front and back, over and beyond.

Then for a vague moment a mocking little figure squirmed into shape before his eyes. He plunged toward it—and his sword quivered up to its hilt in the wooden beams of the bridge. With fumbling hands he wrenched it loose, but a smart stab between the ankles sent him thudding down upon the planks again. Yoshisune picked up Benkei's sword, flitted to the top of the fence, and taunted, "Such a wretched fighter! You demanded my sword and now I have yours. But it's a poor weapon—I scorn to keep it. Here." And the sword rattled down to Benkei's side.

Baffled, humiliated, the giant picked it up and began to replace it in his scabbard. The boy leaped down from the fence, took out his flute, and played the first notes of a merry tune as he started on his way.

In a flash Benkei wheeled and cut at him. "Impudent child...!" But Yoshisune was already on the gate again.

This was too much for Benkei. For the first time in his life he turned and ran. But before he reached the edge of the bridge another blow tripped him neatly, tumbling him down on all fours like a grunting wild boar. His sword sailed skyward, and then he felt the lad perch on his shoulder as lightly as a butterfly.

"Cut off my head!" wailed the giant. "No longer can I bear to live! But first, Master, tell me your name."

"Kill you?" said Yoshisune softly. "No. Live to be my henchman and to fight with me against the Taira when the time comes. For I am Yoshisune, son of Yoshidomo, and prince of the Minamoto."

A Minamoto! Happiness flowed over Benkei in a suffocating flood. How he hated the oppressive Taira clan and longed for a champion to lead the Minamoto against them! Here was a leader who could command his complete respect, loyalty, and love. Benkei suddenly felt as if he—the Black Priest of the Western Pagoda—had come home at last from a long, aimless journey.

"Where you go, Master," he whispered, "I will go: to triumph or defeat, joy or misery, life or death."

"Then take my sword," said Yoshisune. "Should not a henchman of the Minamoto carry the sword of the Minamoto?"

The thousandth sword! Benkei put it into his scabbard and followed his lord into the night.

A samurai of old Japan was both a warrior skilled in swordsmanship and a gentleman versed in music, literature, and courtly manners. The samurai referred to contemptuously by Benkei were Taira who had succumbed to the lure of luxurious living in Kyoto. But a true samurai was loyal, brave, and devoted, ready to die for his master at any time.

chohan, the ROBBER chieftain

Now Yoshisune knew that his days in the monastery must come to an end—and soon. Like the plaintive melody of a flute, one thought wandered endlessly in his mind: "I am a Minamoto. What have I to do with the cloisters and shaded groves of a monastery? To become a warrior and to vanquish the Taira— that is my destiny!" Then the echo of the Tengu king's strident voice would cut across his consciousness: "You shall live forever as the greatest swordsman in Japan. Go, for there is nothing more I can teach you!"

There was little more that the learned priests could teach Yoshisune either, for an absorbing zest for study had already made him master of all the ancient volumes in the monastery. "After reading a book once he can recite it from memory, and a second reading gives him complete understanding," reported his teacher to the other priests. Even the oldest monks admitted that the youth had learned the Buddhist Wheel of the Law better than they.

Then one day Yoshisune heard that preparations were being made to shave his head and invest him with monastic robes. To avenge his father he must be a warrior, not a priest! He must go at once. But where?

The answer to his unspoken question came one night as he prayed in the temple for guidance. A wizened old trader sidled up to him and, mingling barely audible whispers with the lad's fervent appeal to the deity, he said: "I come from Hidehira, military chieftain and friend of your father. He bids me say that the son of Minamoto Yoshidomo will be welcome in his realm far up in the North Country. There is much you can learn from him about the arts of war. Tonight at the hour of the rat my caravan leaves from the grove at the base of Kurama." Without waiting for an answer, the old trader shuffled away and was lost among the worshippers.

Swiftly Yoshisune sent the message to Benkei: "Wait for me here. I travel to the North Country. When the time comes I shall send for you, and together we will fight for the Minamoto."

That night Yoshisune crept from his tiny room and made his way down the twisting mountain path to the grove, where a group of traveling merchants waited. The old trader brought forward a spirited horse with a gold-flecked saddle. "For you, prince of the Minamoto," he said as he helped the boy mount. Prince of the Minamoto! Yoshisune's heart swelled. Then, with a silent goodbye to the mountains that had nurtured him so well, he took his place in the long caravan of horsemen and pack mules.

Danger rode with them, for soon their route led up through rough, bandit-infested country. As the caravan coiled along precipitous mountain trails, the faces of the merchants grew tense and their hands jerked nervously at their weapons. "We are entering the haunts of the robber chieftain Chohan," the old trader said. "For years his murderous band has made travel through these mountains a nightmare. For ferocity and strength, Chohan has no equal. Like a vulture he sweeps down on caravans, and once in his talons no man lives. Watch sharply, young prince, and pray!"

Vigilant, fearful, the merchants traversed the treacherous mountain trails, sensing rather than seeing the evil eyes that peered at them through the thicket or from sentinel posts high among the rocks. But at last the caravan came to a village inn at the base of the hills. Rejoicing, the men feasted and drank late into the night, certain that they had eluded the dreaded Chohan.

But to Yoshisune the innkeeper seemed furtive, and the serving girls cast nervous glances at the packs containing the merchants' silks and gold. Something was wrong. The youth said nothing to his companions, but after they had gone to bed he slipped out to the gateway of the inn. He was right! There had been good reason for uneasiness! Toward him through the trees was skulking a large band of men, their swords and daggers unsheathed.

Stealing back to the entrance, Yoshisune hid behind a screen. Ah, here would be a fight! Too bad that Benkei had to miss it!

A few minutes later two of the bandits slunk through the doorway, their lanterns casting a wavering light into the dim courtyard. A whirr—and heads and lanterns rolled to the ground. Two more men came, and their heads tumbled down beside the

others. Then heads began to bounce from shoulders like rain-drops from mountain rocks as the entire band swarmed into the enclosure.

From all sides the thieves rushed upon Yoshisune to cut him to ribbons, but he was like water running through their fingers or a tantalizing breeze in their faces. Again and again they closed in on him, only to discover that they were clashing against each other while their tiny assailant was slicing off heads at the edge of the circle.

At last Chohan himself leaped through the gate, his hair bris-tling, his face scarlet, and his glaring eyes as fiercely bright as two mirrors in the sun. A roar died on his lips and he stood trans-fixed, gaping in disbelief. This couldn't be happening! The courtyard was strewn with the bodies of his calloused, savage crew. Two of his toughest men, wild-eyed with terror, were running pell mell toward the entrance, babbling something about a "demon fencer." Their pursuer? A mere boy, not more than fifteen years of age!

Yoshisune came to a halt before the seven-foot creature looming in the doorway. Surmising that this was the villainous old chieftain who had brought death to so many innocent travelers, Yoshisune bowed in mock courtesy and said, "You are late, but not *too* late. Stick out your head!"

A strangled bellow burst from Chohan. This weakling! This child...! He sprang, sword whistling through the air. Yoshisune ducked under the weapon and with one deft thrust carved off Chohan's breastplate. Chuckling with delight, the lad leaped backwards ten feet, surveyed the situation critically for an instant, and then flew around to nip off the back guard. Almost at the moment that it clanged to the floor, the right thigh shield tumbled beside it. Stupefied, Chohan—the unrivaled, unchallenged fighting terror of the hills—saw his elfin assailant dodge one murderous blow after another to carve off chunks of metal, until the entire armor lay in a heap on the floor.

But now Yoshisune was tired of play. A final stab, and the wicked Chohan was no more.

The merchants and villagers, roused by the din, watched in silent amazement as Yoshisune replaced his sword in its scabbard, picked his way through the cluttered courtyard, and went to bed. Was this incredible youth who had destroyed an entire band of thieves a human being or a Tengu? Whichever he was, with him fighting for the Minamoto, the red flag of the Taira was certain to wave less boldly in the breeze.

197

The Japanese, like the Chinese, write their family name first, given name last: hence, Minamoto Yoshisune.

the bell of miidera

198　　Months passed, and then Benkei received the message: "Come.
The time is now." This was what he had been living for! His
one desire ever since the fight on the bridge had been to serve
and—if necessary—die for his young master. Great adventures
ahead: what joy to share them with Yoshisune!

But as Benkei strode up the winding path to his hut on
Mount Hiei to make final preparations, he became thoughtful.
Soon he would leave these hills forever and perhaps never again
see the monks who had taught him to read. What had he done
in return? He owed them a parting favor.

Sitting on a ledge in front of his hut, he let his eyes travel up
the slopes of the mountain beyond, where the monasteries of
Miidera nestled. Just then the great bell of Miidera tolled, send-
ing a shower of golden melody into the forest-scented air.

Benkei leaped to his feet. That was it! Long had his brother
monks on Mount Hiei envied the Miidera priests their bell.
They need envy no longer! Bounding into his hut, he found a
paper lantern. With it in one hand and his twelve-foot spear
in the other, he started down the mountain.

The bell had just sounded out the hour of the ox when a
giant figure crept from the brush, climbed up into the wooden
tower, and went to work. Deftly fastening a truss of heavy ropes
about the bell, he loosed it from its moorings.

A soft swish of a woman's skirts riveted him to attention.
He was not alone! Someone was watching! He peered into the

darkness but could see nothing. For a moment he hesitated, then turned doggedly back to his work. But the hands that finally lowered the huge weight from the tower were clammy.

Just as he tied the bell to one end of his spear and the paper lantern to the other, he again heard the peculiar swishing sound. Then, despite the blackness of the night, he saw the ghostly form of a maiden. Directly in his path she stood, holding out her hands beseechingly.

Benkei's spine tingled and his hair stood up like the bristles of a boar. He ducked to cut off the sight of the shadowy figure and then, hoisting the bell over his back, staggered down the mountain. And the sweat that poured down into his whiskers was not from exertion alone, for Benkei knew that the maiden was the spirit of the Miidera bell, begging him not to take her away.

Bent double under his heavy burden, he reached the foot of the mountain. But this was only the easier part of his task, for now he must cross through the valley and struggle up the steep incline of Mount Hiei. His brother monks had better be grateful. "Such hard, dirty work!" muttered Benkei.

He reached the monastery at last and put down the bell. Now to surprise the monks with his gift. Never would they forget this day. He clanged his sword against the bell—and then jumped. For instead of tolling forth its usual enchanting tones, it wailed, "I want to go home! I want to go home!"

Benkei was stunned. Then a sudden twinge in his muscles reminding him of that seven-mile trek up and down mountains with the enormous object in tow, he became angry.

"All that work and now you won't ring?" he shouted. In a rage he again struck the bell; again it sobbed, more sadly than before, "I want to go home! I want to go home!"

"You're mocking me!" screamed Benkei. "I'll *make* you ring as any respectable temple bell should!" But the harder he struck the louder it insisted, "I want to go home!"

Infuriated beyond endurance, the big priest lifted the bell to his shoulders and hurled it down the mountainside.

The next morning as he strolled into the valley below, he came across a group of priests standing around a battered bronze bell and moaning dismally.

"What's this?" asked Benkei.

"Oh," grieved one of the priests, "last night malicious demons stole our bell. Here it is, but we can't get it back up the mountain."

"What would you give to have it restored to your pagoda?" demanded Benkei.

"Anything!" chorused the priests.

"Would you give a pot of bean soup as large as this bell, filled as many times as a man could empty it at one sitting?"

"Gladly, but even a giant like you couldn't carry a bell weighing half a ton up that mountain."

Without another word, Benkei marched back up to his hut, picked up his spear and lantern, and returned to the priests, who were still mourning and wringing their hands in despair.

Again fastening the lantern on one end of his spear and the bell on the other, Benkei rolled the immense weight onto his shoulder and puffed up the mountain to Miidera. The priests trailed behind, full of wonder and worry—worry about all that bean soup.

Depositing the bell in the tower, Benkei hurried to the monastery kitchen. The priests had already pulled out their third largest kettle and were preparing to fill it, when Benkei roared, "Scoundrels! This isn't your biggest pot! By the gods I'll eat from one large enough to fill my stomach or your bell will go sailing down into the valley again!"

Clattering among the cupboards, the giant hauled out a cauldron huge as the bell itself—the one used to feed all the priests on the mountain during their sacred festivals. "Fill it!" he bellowed, and the priests jumped about like grasshoppers to appease the fiery giant whose roars made every dish and pot in the kitchen rattle.

All morning Benkei ate soup; all afternoon he ate soup; and when the moon grinned through the shutters late that night he was still eating soup. Again and again the big pot was filled, until the summer supplies of the entire monastery were exhausted. Still the giant showed no signs of stopping, and the priests had to scurry all over the mountain to get more beans.

About noon of the second day, Benkei put down the pot, rubbed his stomach, and said, "A good meal—one to really sustain a man." Then, in deep satisfaction at having had enough to eat for once, he sank his teeth deep into the iron rim of the pot. Beaming at the weary monks, he ambled off down the mountain, his stomach filled with bean soup and his ears filled with the sweet and contented chiming of the Miidera bell.

Now to join Yoshisune in the North Country. Ah, life was good, mused Benkei.

The Miidera bell was the very one given by the Dragon King to Hidesato, My Lord Bag of Rice, as a reward for his killing the gigantic centipede. To this day the bell and the tooth-marked cauldron can be seen at the old monastery at Miidera.

Many legends grew up about the bell. One was that an insane woman who touched it would be instantly restored to her wits. A criminal who touched it would be unable to free himself. Another legend accounted for its dull surface. In the old days it had shone like a mirror, but one day a beautiful woman climbed upon it, wishing she had so lustrous a mirror for herself. As she admired her reflection and played her hands around it, the metal shrank from her fingers and has been dull and corroded ever since.

Some interesting Japanese sculpture shows Benkei carrying the thousand-pound bell on his back.

the fortress of ichinotani

"Great news, Benkei! Yoritomo, my elder half-brother, has escaped from exile and has established himself as head of the Minamoto clan. We go at once to join him!"

"Ah, Master, during these many months that you have been here in the North Country learning the strategy of war from Hidehira, I have lived for this moment alone."

Benkei ran his eyes approvingly over his young master who had just come to welcome him. The kind old ruler Hidehira had supplied the youth with clothes and trappings well befitting a prince of the Minamoto. Yoshisune's robe and skirt were of red brocade decorated in silver and fringed with Chinese green silk. His armor was sewed with purple thread, and a dragon frontlet arched from his helmet. At his back was a quiver of black arrows, and a gold-ornamented sword rested in the deerskin sheath at his side. The saddle of the splendid war horse from which he had just dismounted sparkled with intricate gold designs.

Benkei grinned. This Yoshisune looked as elegant and dashing as one of Kyoto's pampered nobles, but that he was as swift and deadly as a tornado a certain priest who used to call himself the Tengu king could readily testify.

"If ever you need help, come back. Here in my realm you will always find refuge and support." With these parting words of Hidehira in their ears, Benkei and Yoshisune rode forward to meet Yoritomo. Behind them came a retinue of men supplied by the generous old ruler.

Civil war, like an ugly two-headed monster, was already ravaging the land when Yoshisune reached the court of his half-brother. Thousands of warriors, no longer able to endure the tyranny of the Taira, had flocked to the white banners of Yoritomo, and he needed a general to lead his forces in the south and west. Shrewdly he appraised the skill and cleverness of this younger brother who had shown up so opportunely. Yoshisune's moment had come.

Old Hidehira had taught the youth well, and now—with Yoritomo's armies at his back and Benkei at his side—he proved himself to be a brilliant commander. The agility of his mind matched that of his body, and with cunning strategy he led the Minamoto into one victory after another. Before his determined and daring onslaughts the enemy wavered and fell back in confusion from one vantage point after another.

Finally, unable to resist the might of Yoshisune's forces, the harassed Taira withdrew from the capital city, mustered all their strength, and moved to the great fortress of Ichinotani. Here they built fortifications for their entire host of 100,000. The stronghold was considered to be impregnable. The front, protected by the sea, bristled with thousands of ships. To left and right rose barricades that neither man nor beast could penetrate. At the rear were mountains so steep that not even apes could clamber down their crags. In this stronghold the Taira felt that they could rest in complete safety until they were ready to take the offensive. They did not know Yoshisune.

Calling his council together, the young commander announced, "We are going to attack Ichinotani." An incredulous murmur rippled and then swelled through the room. An old warrior Kajiwara jumped to his feet.

"That is unthinkable, my lord!" he blazed. "The Taira are 100,000 strong at Ichinotani; we are only 60,000. Furthermore, we cannot break through their barriers."

"If we are in the minority and their fortress so strong," replied Yoshisune tartly, "what madness to wait until they decide to

attack us! A hesitating tiger is inferior to an active wasp. We shall proceed to Ichinotani at once!"

Kajiwara bit his lip to stifle an angry retort. How dared this young upstart challenge the judgment of so seasoned a warrior as he! This insult he would never forget!

"But, my lord," persisted another warrior in consternation, "the Taira stronghold is like a rock on all sides. From which direction can we attack?"

"Men say that the mountains above Ichinotani are impassable. Therefore the Taira will never expect us from that side. That is where we will strike."

The captains looked at each other aghast. Then their stern faces began to relax as the vibrant confidence of Yoshisune swept through the room like a living flame. Under this dauntless commander, could anything but glory and victory lie ahead? On to Ichinotani!

Swiftly marshaling his forces for the daring attack, Yoshisune led them through unmarked countryside to the base of mountains so jagged and flaring that they seemed to leer contemptuously at the puny men and horses at their base. Rough brambles sheathed the foothills in an unending upward sweep until checked by saw-toothed cliffs and gaping chasms. It was at the other side of this formidable barrier that the enemy lay.

Gingerly the men hacked into the trackless underbrush, beating back the brambles inch by inch. Over concealed boulders and through icy brooks they fought their way, dragging snorting horses behind them.

As the company wormed higher up the steep inclines, sharp winds bit into hands and faces, and the encrusted snow was like a death shroud waiting to receive the stubborn warriors when they should cease at last to struggle.

Staggering with exhaustion, the half-frozen men reached the summit. But when they looked down on the other side, cries of dismay broke from their rasped throats. The bluffs were as sharp-edged as daggers, and the slopes beyond offered no foothold.

"Impossible," said the officers. "We must go back."

Back! The word was like a whiplash across the numbed faces.

"Wait!" commanded Yoshisune, for his keen eye had caught sight of Benkei, who—always ahead of the others—was coming back toward them with a grizzled old hunter.

"Is there a path down the precipice?" asked Yoshisune.

The old man shook his head. "I know these mountains very well," he said. "No horse can descend those craggy slopes."

"But can a stag go down?" persisted Yoshisune.

The hunter scratched his nose thoughtfully. "That stags do pass is certain," he said, "for in winter I have seen them in the pastures below."

"Where a stag can go a horse can!" shouted Yoshisune. "Keep tight rein, my men, and after me. Those of you whose mounts

206

were lost or hurt as we climbed the mountain must slide down on your sleeping mats." Riding to the top of the cliff, he urged his reluctant horse over its brim.

The men hesitated: they were willing to die fighting, but there was nothing glorious about breaking their necks and lying unburied on these barren rocks. Even Benkei looked alarmed, but sternly he motioned the men to follow their commander. No one ever argued with Benkei. Up and over the cliff swept the horsemen, the soldiers with only grass mats following in their wake.

So steep was the incline that the stirrups of the men behind struck against helmets or armor of the ones in front. So terrifying were the vistas before them that valiant warriors shut their eyes in sick fear. Thousands of men at the mercy of a mountain...

Benkei had stayed behind to prod the less stouthearted warriors. Hardly had be begun his descent when his horse wounded its leg on a sharp rock. Grumbling under his breath about "more

207

dirty work," the giant hoisted the animal to his shoulders and
continued his journey down the cliff.

The Taira, lolling in their stronghold below, gradually became
aware of a distant crashing and roaring. Puzzled, they stared
about them. Then someone shrieked, "Look! The mountain!"
All eyes jerked upward. Screams of horror burst from every
throat. The gaunt slopes were alive with mounted demons—or
were the creatures dropping from the clouds!

In frenzied terror the Taira snatched their weapons and ran.
The ships! They alone offered escape from the hordes streaming
from the skies. Comrades trampled comrades in that mad flight
to the sea. Scores of warriors swarmed into vessels meant for the
few. Ships tipped and overturned even while more men, clinging to the sides and struggling to climb aboard, were mercilessly
beaten off by their fellow Taira. Duty to father, brother, or lord
was forgotten: only escape was important. Three overloaded
ships moved slowly out to sea and then sank into the depths.
Only an occasional vessel plowed to safety through the mass of
screaming, struggling humanity.

On the shore, flames crackled riotously as the exultant Minamoto raced through the fortress with firebrands. Savage hand-to-
hand fighting raged along the entire shore, and many a warrior
forced the enemy from the skies to pay dearly for that moment
of triumph.

Not every Taira had joined in the flight to the ships. On a sand dune stood Noritsune, champion archer of the Taira. Arrow after arrow spun from his bow toward the Minamoto, and so swift and sure were his shafts that he was able to maintain a cleared space between himself and the enemy through which his fellow clansmen could flee to the waters.

But as the clouds of smoke thickened, one of Noritsune's faithful retainers crept to his side. "My lord, the ships are leaving. Soon there will be no chance of escape. Save yourself that you may fight again for the Taira."

Noritsune shook his head. "No, Rokuro," he said, "many a Minamoto has already tasted my arrows, but the quiver is not yet empty."

Again Rokuro pleaded. "My life is of little worth, yours of infinite value to the clan. Give me your armor and helmet that I may hold the enemy at bay while you go to the ships."

Duty to his clan! Nothing else could have swayed the brave Noritsune. He accepted the sacrifice. Behind the shelter of Rokuro's arrows, the famous archer slipped into the water and made his way to a vessel moving out to sea.

Dressed now in his lord's armor, the samurai shouted, "Come, Minamoto! I, Noritsune, defy you!" The Minamoto heard that

voice and held back. One did not willingly face the champion archer of the Taira. Not until the last arrow was gone from the quiver of the supposed Noritsune and he had slumped to the ground under a barrage of deadly shafts did the Minamoto dare advance to the dune. They snatched off the helmet and looked into the face, not of the champion, but of the faithful samurai who had died for his master.

Farther down the shore the Minamoto warrior Kumagai was hot in pursuit of some fleeing Taira when he saw a single horseman who had swum his horse out twenty yards from the water's edge and was attempting to reach the ships. His gold-emblazoned armor and helmet surmounted with horns identified him at once as a nobleman—a prisoner of whom one could boast.

"Stop!" shouted Kumagai. "Shameful to show an enemy your back!" The horseman wheeled around immediately and made his way to the shore. "I am ready for you, Minamoto!" he cried.

Swords clashed. In minutes the powerful Kumagai had hurled the Taira to the ground and torn off his helmet. Why, it was a mere boy, not more than sixteen, that he had felled! A boy the age of his own son! As the old warrior looked at the youth's handsome face, pity wrenched his heart.

"What is your name? Speak, for I would spare your life."

"No, tell me first who you are," said the Taira imperiously.

"I am Kumagai, a Minamoto of no superior rank."

"Then you have done yourself great honor," said the boy, "for I am Atsumori, nephew of the Taira chieftain Kiyomori."

Kiyomori's nephew! A prize above all prizes! But how pitiful to put him to death! In anguish Kumagai remembered how he had grieved when his own young son had been wounded.

211

"Get up," said the old warrior with sudden resolution. "Go to the ships." At that moment the sound of pounding hoofbeats made him look up. Too late. Bearing down upon them were fifty Minamoto horsemen.

Tears streamed down Kumagai's face as he turned again to the Taira. "Alas," he said, "though I would spare you, there is no escape from my fellow Minamoto. You must die, but let it be quickly by my hand and I will pray for your soul."

"Let it be so," replied the youth. "I am ready."

With a sword that trembled in his grasp, Kumagai slew the boy. Stripping the body of its armor, he discovered a brocade bag containing a flute. This bright-faced youth had taken a musical instrument to war with him—and he, Kumagai, had slain him! Heartbroken, the old warrior turned and rode away. Never again would he raise his hand in battle, but would end his days as a Buddhist monk.

At the Kurodani Monastery there is a body of water called the "Armor Pool," because it was here that Kumagai threw his battle attire when he renounced the life of a warrior and became a monk. The story of his encounter with Atsumori is the subject of a famous No drama.

dannoura

Before the battle of Ichinotani the red flags of the Taira had floated over fourteen provinces, and the clan was feared and obeyed. But now, after the destruction of their stronghold, they were scattered and homeless. Desperately they struggled to rally their broken forces and to make a new stand. But their schemes were futile: always Yoshisune was a step ahead, an attack ahead, anticipating them at every turn.

Driven, harried, no longer safe on land, the Taira were compelled to collect the remnants of their fleet and put to sea. With them they took the lords and ladies of the court, the Child-Emperor Antoku, and the Three Sacred Treasures of the realm—the mirror, the sword, and the jewels. With the emperor and the treasures in their possession, they were still the legitimate rulers, in name at least.

From harbor to harbor they went but no one would receive them, for the cruel tentacles of the Taira had reached deeply into Japan. Then they sailed among the small islands that clustered about the mainland, waiting helplessly for the dreadful moment they knew must come—the moment when Yoshisune would strike again.

The fleet, forced to stay close to land, was constantly watched. Day by day fishermen brought word to the Minamoto of the Taira position, and it was when the enemy had sailed to Dannoura at the western end of the Inland Sea that Yoshisune again called his generals together.

"The time is now," he said. "We will assemble our ships at once and crush the foe at Dannoura."

Again it was Kajiwara who spoke first. Never for a moment had he forgotten Yoshisune's imperious rejection of his advice about attacking Ichinotani, and the success of that daring campaign had only increased his resentment against the young commander. But here was another chance for him, a veteran warrior, to instruct this bumptious youth in the ways of war.

"My lord, the Taira are more experienced seamen than we," he said. "Attacking them will not be easy. I propose that we place oars at both ends of our boats to ensure our swift retreat as well as our swift advance."

213

Yoshisune stiffened. Retreat! The idea—the very word—was intolerable to him. "We will not even think of retreat," he said. "Always we will advance to victory."

"These are the tactics of a wild boar, not of a warrior!" rejoined Kajiwara hotly.

"Better a wild boar than a coward!"

Kajiwara said no more, but hatred twisted like a serpent through his veins. How much longer must he bow to the command of this cocksure stripling young enough to be his grandson!

Yoshisune was continuing: "We shall not wait for good weather. In storm, when the Taira do not expect us, we shall call on them."

The orders were issued, but the sailors refused to take boats into the lashing waters. "I will convince them," said Benkei, and with several strong retainers he marched down to the shore. Soon he returned. "They see things differently now, Master," and he fingered the heavy club at his side.

It was in a cold, rainy dawn that the Taira watchmen caught sight of the Minamoto fleet coming toward them through the mist. All night the Taira ships had reared and plunged in the storm-whipped waves that seemed intent on whirling them against the rocky islands. But now a far greater danger loomed: Yoshisune had come!

War drums sounded the alarm; warriors leaped to their posts; ships were hastily formed into three battle lines, those containing the child-emperor, the court ladies, and the old men being taken

to the rear. On the front line of ships five hundred of the best bowmen took their stand, shoulder to shoulder. Overhead, the red banners writhed in the gale; underneath, the waves slapped menacingly.

Now the battle cry of the Minamoto tore through the air, and the Taira answered with a volley of five hundred arrows. Men screamed and fell back from that first fierce assault, but others took their places. Relentlessly the Minamoto ships moved forward.

On the foremost Taira vessel stood the champion archer Noritsune. Arrows lashed from his bow like shafts of rain in a summer torrent as he strained for a sight of the Minamoto he hated most. Through his veins burned one resolve: to kill with his own hands the clever, elusive Yoshisune who had reduced the proud Taira to miserable fugitives.

Benkei, standing beside his master in the front ranks of the Minamoto fleet, whistled under his breath. "These Taira fight like fiends today!"

"They are resisting black, inevitable fate," replied Yoshisune. "But how I wish that the mighty Noritsune were fighting under my command! He will demand a high price for our victory." And Yoshisune's hand faltered momentarily on the string of his bow as he looked at the men who had already fallen.

A sudden lurch of the boat caused him to drop his bow overboard. Without a moment's hesitation he dived into the water to retrieve it.

"Master," reproved Benkei as Yoshisune scrambled into the boat again, "how could you risk your valuable life for so trivial a thing as a bow?"

"I would not let it fall into the hands of the enemy," replied Yoshisune, "lest they laugh when they see how small it is. Honor means more to me than life."

A shrill cry interrupted him. "Look! The sacred doves of the war god Hachiman!" Every eye turned upward, and the hiss of arrows ceased as Taira and Minamoto watched breathlessly.

Circling both fleets, the two white doves came to rest at last on the shrine of the god on Yoshisune's vessel. An anguished wail rose from the Taira: "Hachiman fights with the Minamoto!"

Then the sky opened and a white banner descended to the masthead of Yoshisune's ship. His own flag fluttered up into the heavens and was enveloped by the clouds.

"But look! Still another omen!" On the crest of the waves came a shoal of hundreds of dolphins. Frisking and leaping, they surrounded the Taira fleet.

"What can this mean? cried the Taira chieftain. "Is there still hope? Can this be an omen for good?"

An old diviner pushed through to the side of the boat. For a breathless moment he looked at the dolphins and then said, "If they go back, we will be destroyed, but if they stay, victory is ours."

The word flew from ship to ship and hope surged wildly in every Taira breast, only to be eclipsed with despair as the dolphins—with a final flourish of tails—dived under the fleet and were gone.

On one of the Taira vessels stood Shigeyoshi, his eyes dark and brooding. For three years he had been a supporter of the Taira. Now, as the dolphins disappeared, carrying with them the last hopes of the clan, he slipped into the water and swam to the enemy fleet. The god had decided in favor of the Minamoto: then he, Shigeyoshi, must have made a mistake and would therefore shift his allegiance.

The strategy of the Taira had been to put the strongest warriors on the largest ships so that the Minamoto would be induced to attack them first in the belief that the commanders and champions were there. Then the Taira planned to whip their smaller craft into a ring about the enemy. But when Shigeyoshi revealed the scheme to the Minamoto, they swung about to attack the lighter ships. Now the clash of swords split the air as the Minamoto jumped from their own vessels to those of the Taira for hand-to-hand fighting.

Yoshisune was commanding these activities from a ship on
which he stood alone, when suddenly he had a premonition of
danger. He whirled. Noritsune was charging down upon him!

Throughout the battle the keen-eyed archer champion had
watched every move that Yoshisune made. Now, seeing that the
young commander was alone, he had brought his ship alongside
and had leaped aboard. Noritsune's moment of triumph had
come.

He sprang, his great hands outspread to crush out the life of
his enemy. Like a whiplash Yoshisune ripped into action, mind

and body instantly keyed to combat this mortal danger. In wrestling, his slender body would be no match for that of the iron-muscled Noritsune, nor was there even time to unsheathe his sword. Decision and action were simultaneous: with a lithe twist of his body, Yoshisune slipped through the hungry hands of the champion, leaped to the rail, and soared across an eighteen-foot expanse to the next boat. Landing as lightly as a bird, he raised his spear aloft and laughed at the Taira archer, whose curved fingers clutched convulsively at space.

Fury and admiration strove for mastery of Noritsune. His chance had come—and his hands were still empty. But that leap! Had he really witnessed it, or had he dreamed the impossible?

A thud awakened the Taira from his stunned reverie. He turned to see a Minamoto boat come alongside. From it bounded a powerful captain and two brawny wrestlers who had seen the attempt on their commander's life.

A half-smile flitted across Noritsune's face as he waited for them: he could not leap eighteen feet after Yoshisune, but for strength he had no equal. He caught the first man around the waist and tossed him overboard. Then he grasped the other two in his arms and leaped into the sea. Together they went down and did not rise again. And so perished the valiant Noritsune.

At the end of the long line of Taira ships stood Niidono, guardian of the eight-year-old Emperor Antoku. She had seen one vessel after another fall to the enemy. Soon the Minamoto would be swarming over the decks of this one also and would dare lay hands on the child-emperor.

Niidono knew what she must do. Though but a woman, she could protect her young sovereign from shame. She donned a robe of white silk, tied the sacred sword to her belt and put the casket containing the sacred jewels under her arm. Then she led Antoku to the side of the boat.

"Where are you taking me?" asked the child.

Tears streamed from her eyes as she answered, "Perhaps you do not know that you have been born to the imperial throne. But an evil destiny now claims you. So now, turn to the east and bid farewell to the deity of the Great Shrine of Ise. Then turn to the west and pray that Amida Buddha may welcome you to the great Western Land. This world trembles with sorrow, but beneath the waves is a realm of perfect happiness. It is there that we are going."

Antoku bound his long black hair up in his robe and clasped his hands together, turning first to east and then to west to pray as he had been told. "I am ready," he said.

Taking him in her arms and whispering, "It is my honor to escort my lord to the new capital in the ocean depths," Niidono sank with him into the waves.

When the Minamoto reached the boat and clambered over its decks, they found little there except a few frightened court ladies and old men, for many had followed their emperor and his guardian into the sea. One lady of the court had been on the point of leaping overboard with a casket containing the third of the imperial treasures, the sacred mirror, when an arrow pinned her skirt to the side of the ship. Rough Minamoto soldiers seized and held her back. One of them knocked off the lid of the casket, only to find a smaller silk-wrapped box inside. But as he attempted to remove it, his eyes were darkened and blood gushed from his nose. Everyone in the boat became dizzy and faint.

"Do not open the box!" warned one of the Taira. "It contains the sacred mirror that no profane eye may behold!" Minamoto soldiers, so brave a moment before, trembled.

The Taira host had perished. The sea was red with their banners, and their deserted ships tossed aimlessly on the waves. But the ghosts of their leaders continued to haunt the strait. Mysterious fires gleamed on the water, and the din of battle reverberated through the air. At last, to pacify the spirits, a temple and a cemetery were built close by. When the armor and swords of the Taira had been collected and deposited there, the waters again became safe for mariners. The common soldiers, however, still wander the beaches and hills in the shape of tiny crabs whose shells are clearly marked with the features of infuriated warriors.

Yoshisune's eighteen-foot jump is famous in Japanese drama, art, and literature. It is sometimes referred to as the "eight-boat jump" because some legends say that the amazing little warrior cleared eight boats and landed in the ninth.

The sacred sword that sank into the sea with Niidono and Antoku was lost for many generations. How it was finally restored to the Japanese emperors is told later. The casket containing the sacred jewels, however, floated on the waves and was recovered. Together with the mirror it came back into the possession of the imperial family. At present the mirror lies in Ise Shrine, the sword in Atsuta Temple, and the jewels—together with replicas of the mirror and sword—in the imperial palace in Tokyo.

Nagato Province is famous for its "Taira Family" crabs.

triumph and treachery

Triumphantly the Minamoto swept into the capital city of Kyoto, bringing back two of the three Sacred Treasures and the realization that the Taira were gone forever. Yoshisune was welcomed as a gallant hero and a military genius, and his lamp of fame glowed even more brilliantly when he restored order to the realm so that people once more felt safe.

Now the young general who had braved the hardships of precipitous mountains, biting winds, and chaotic seas luxuriated in the gay and comfortable life of the capital. No longer was a helmet his pillow nor the wild countryside his home. He lived in a mansion built of the finest woods, and its silk screens and thick mats were the best that the artisans of Kyoto could produce. His robes were of embroidered silk, and his teeth were blackened and his face painted in the most fashionable manner. In a lacquered palanquin borne on the shoulders of smartly dressed carriers, and followed by a glittering train of attendants, he took leisurely rides about the city or into the country to view the flowers or the fireflies.

There was time to play the flute and to write the tiny poems called tanka—pursuits dear to the hearts of the leisured nobles and ladies of the elegant capital city. And there was time to love and to marry enchanting little Shizuka, the most exquisite dancing girl in Kyoto.

Shizuka's beauty was like that of a single radiant star against a velvet sky. Her oval face was framed with raven hair that fell in rippling cascade to her feet, and the slender body moved with the grace of a willow branch in a caressing breeze.

But it was Shizuka's dancing rather than her beauty that had made her famous throughout Japan. At one time when the country was harassed with drought so severe that leaf and fern shriveled to dust, she had danced a prayer for relief. The gods had been pleased with her sensitive posturing, singing, and use of the fan. In torrents the rain had come, reviving parched fields and gardens. The emperor had rewarded her with a costly robe, and grateful people throughout the realm had honored her name.

Not for long, however, were Yoshisune and Shizuka to enjoy luxury and ease. In Kamakura, where Yoritomo had established himself as Shogun, or military dictator, poisonous clouds of evil began to form. Kajiwara, still brooding, still bitter against Yoshisune for not honoring his counsel before the battles of Ichinotani and Dannoura, saw his chance for revenge. What better way than to plant suspicion in the mind of Yoritomo that his younger brother was disloyal, waiting only for the opportune moment to seize supreme power in his own hands? It would be so easy. Were not the people of Kyoto loud in their acclaim of Yoshisune? Had not Kajiwara himself heard them say that the young commander was the most brilliant man in the country and that the older brother had done little by comparison?

Yoritomo listened to old Kajiwara's stories, and his face grew livid with anger. How had Yoshisune dared such impudence and disloyalty! Was it not he, Yoritomo, who had supplied the armies and ships? Was he now to be supplanted as head of the Minamoto by this ambitious younger brother?

"Work fast, my lord," urged Kajiwara. "Who knows but that the arrogant Yoshisune, who people say can do what he wants with Japan, will come down here to Kamakura next? You have no time to lose."

Yoritomo bowed his head, torn with conflicting emotions. He could not have established himself as Shogun without his half-brother's aid. Yet those accusations...

Kajiwara, watching intently the effect of his words on the troubled prince, hitched up closer. "Once long ago I saved you from humiliation and death. I want only to do so again, my lord."

Yoritomo remembered well that day. His mind raced back to the time when he had escaped from the island to which the Taira chieftain Kiyomori had exiled him years before. Alone and friendless, he had fled through the woods, with the Taira close behind. When exhaustion made it impossible to go further, he had hid himself in a decaying tree trunk. But he had not eluded his enemies for long. In despair—for capture meant certain death —he had heard their pounding feet and excited voices. They were coming directly to his hiding place!

One of the pursuers, Kajiwara, had seen Yoritomo crawl into the tree trunk. In a sudden sweep of sympathy he had resolved to turn against his own clan, the Taira, and to save the enemy prince. Hurrying a bit ahead of the others, he had reached the place first. "I don't believe he came this way at all," he had said. "The two doves on this decayed oak are certainly undisturbed in their billing and cooing, and there is a spider web across the opening. But just to make sure…" With that he had thrust his bow into the tree trunk, carefully avoiding the huddled figure at its far end.

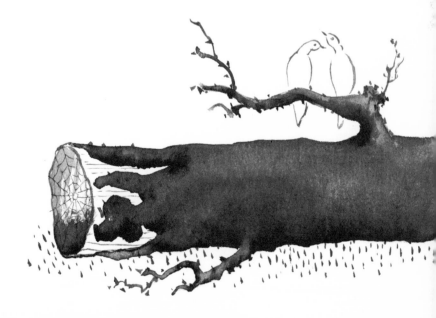

The Taira had gone away, and Yoritomo had lived to rally the Minamoto clan and to make himself the supreme ruling power in Japan. Never had he forgotten Kajiwara's gift of life to him, and the old warrior, renouncing forever his allegiance to the Taira, had become his most trusted and influential advisor.

Now Yoritomo turned to the man at his side and asked sharply, "How shall I dispose of Yoshisune?"

"Through an assassin!" hissed Kajiwara. "Let an assassin pay your half-brother for his treachery!"

Yoritomo hesitated no longer. Determined now that Yoshisune should die, he summoned a strong henchman. "Shoshun, take a large company of men and go to Kyoto as if on a pilgrimage. Conceal your armor and weapons in boxes labeled 'offerings for the shrine.' But when you return, let one of those boxes carry the head of Yoshisune."

Some of Yoshisune's poetry that he presumably wrote while enjoying the life of a nobleman in Kyoto is preserved and quoted to this day.

The high respect accorded to music and poetry in ancient Japan is illustrated by the story of Akoya, a beautiful girl who was accused of giving refuge to a Taira fugitive. No direct evidence against her could be found, nor would she confess. Then she was commanded to come to court in her best robes to play the koto. Akoya improvised a tanka and then played so beautifully that the magistrates were convinced of her innocence. "Fine music and poetry," they said, "can come only from a pure heart."

Hachiman, god of war, was the patron deity of the Minamoto. Because of the two doves that perched on Yoritomo's hiding place, doves have always been sacred to Hachiman and large numbers of them are kept at his numerous shrines throughout Japan.

The title of Shogun, which means "generalissimo," had been created by a member of the Fujiwara family in 930 A.D., but it was Yoritomo who made himself a military dictator under this title and brought all the authority of Japan into his own hands. His capital at Kamakura remained the metropolis of the of the Shogunate for 260 years, and the office of Shogun lasted until 1868, when the power of the emperor was finally restored.

specters, clogs,
and horsetails

Shizuka was uneasy. An elusive little feeling that her husband was in danger wandered persistently through her mind. Rumors that Yoshisune had fallen out of favor with Yoritomo came to her ears from time to time. She had seen the hurt bewilderment on her lord's face as he tried to understand this coolness on the part of the half-brother whom he had served so well.

Then one day a maidservant mentioned that a large band of pilgrims from Kamakura were staying at an inn close to the city gates. Several times the name of Yoshisune and reference to an ugly bit of business had crept into their talk.

Bands of fear tightened around Shizuka's heart. "Get back to the inn," she bade the girl. "Listen closely to the talk of the pilgrims tonight and bring me word of what they say."

The maid hurried away but soon returned, breathless and excited. "The master is in danger!" she panted. "The travelers are already on the way to the palace to kill him!"

Shizuka sped to Yoshisune's apartment. On the threshold she paused. It was not befitting a lady to rush unsummoned into her lord's presence and awaken him. After all, Yoshisune was no ordinary man: he was a great prince of the Minamoto. What was she to do? Then she caught sight of the armor lying beside her sleeping husband. Grasping the breastplate in one hand and an arm shield in the other, she clanged the metal until the sound reverberated through every corner of the palace. In an instant Yoshisune was on his feet, hand reaching for his sword.

"What is it?"

"Enemies at the gate! My maidservant has just brought the news! You are in mortal danger!"

"And now they themselves are in danger!" said Yoshisune. "Summon Benkei and the other retainers while I hold off the villains who so rudely disturb my sleep." Yoshisune sped to the gate, where he saw in the moonlight a band of 150 men. He flung himself upon them.

Benkei, awakened by Shizuka, soused his head in a tub of water to clear it and struggled into his black armor. Seizing his six-foot sword and a huge eight-sided oaken pole studded with iron pegs, he was about to leave the room when he caught sight of some unusually tall clogs made for muddy weather. An idea struck him. "More dirty work for Benkei," he chuckled as he put them on. Then with ponderous tread—punctuated with booming thumps of his oaken pole—Benkei went into the courtyard.

After the first rush, the ruffians had fallen back for a few minutes to reorganize their strategy, no one wanting to offer his head next to the swift sword flashing at the gate. During the brief lull, Yoshisune heard a resounding thump-bump-thump-bump in the stone courtyard behind him. He glanced sideways, and then his head nearly jerked off in surprise. Stomping toward him was the biggest man he had ever seen, or was it a mountain pine miraculously invested with legs?

Yoshisune clenched his fingers more tightly about his sword and prepared to do battle. One hundred and fifty men at the gate and this monster at his back! Why didn't Benkei come! The youth poised himself for a flying leap at the steadily advancing figure; then he heard a hollow voice booming from the black mass: "Am I wrong, or are you Yoshisune, of Minamoto lineage?"

"Benkei!" With profound relief at having the giant apparition on his side rather than at his back, Yoshisune turned jauntily to the gate. For him the battle already seemed over, because with Benkei around enemies lost their heads. "Get the rest of the blackguards for me," he called.

"Ya-a-a," grunted the giant, and he thumped in his tall clogs out into the street just in time to meet a solid front of armed men advancing toward the gate. They came to an abrupt halt. One look at the monstrous figure, and their legs folded like paper; one sweep of his eight-foot pole, and they flattened like floor mats.

Then Benkei caught sight of Shoshun on a black horse some distance to the rear of his men. Riveted to the spot in astonishment and terror, Shoshun could not gather presence of mind enough to flee until the giant had clumped over the sprawled men and was upon him. Regaining his wits at last, Shoshun turned his horse and spurred it to a gallop. But though the hoofs clattered wildly, it did not move forward! Squealing with fear, Shoshun looked behind him. There was the giant—head thrown back and feet braced—holding on to the horse's tail so that the terrified animal could only thrash up and down in one place!

The next thing Shoshun knew was that the giant had leaped onto the horse behind him and was spurring it back to the gate. Then the assassin felt himself being picked up by the scruff of the neck, dangled at the end of a long arm, and carried like a squirming insect into the palace.

Soon Benkei and Yoshisune knew the dreadful truth. A quick search of the ruffian's clothes revealed a written order for Yoshisune's head.

"What Yoritomo did not accomplish with a band of assassins he will accomplish with his armies," said Benkei. "We must leave Kyoto at once."

Yoshisune's shoulders sagged in grief. Loyalty, devotion, service—these had been his gifts to the brother whom he had revered as head of the Minamoto. Jealousy, hatred, treachery—these were the rewards.

At dawn Yoshisune, Benkei, Shizuka, and twelve faithful henchmen left the capital and hastened to the sea. There they secured boats and embarked upon waters as tumultuous as the storms within their hearts.

Ghosts

The boats rocked fitfully on the troubled sea, and each slap
of the waves was like a dagger-thrust at the fugitives. Under the
long, protecting sleeves of her robe, Shizuka clenched and un-
clenched her hands in grief as she brooded over the injustice to
her young lord. Yoshisune sat with bowed head. Yesterday he
had been the second most important man in the realm; today he
was like a hunted animal.

An exclamation of surprise from Benkei aroused Yoshisune
from his sad musings, and he realized that they were sailing into
familiar waters.

"Don't you recognize this place, Master?" asked the giant.

"Not exactly. Where are we, Benkei?"

"Ah, I am surprised that you do not know. We are close to
the spot where we pitched the Taira host into the sea. Just ahead
is Dannoura. But look, Master: does not the sky seem angry? Has
the sea not changed its color? Do you not hear a whispering in
the wind?"

Even while Benkei spoke, a crimson glow on the horizon began
to deepen into a churning, blood-tinged cloud. Like a gigantic
screw boring into the night, it moved forward. Then from its
depths streaked claws of flame that slashed into the waves and
goaded them to screaming fury. Nearer came the fiery cloud, and
now the air was filled with the hiss and clang of arrow and
sword. War drums boomed, and then desolate wails pierced the
night.

Benkei's whiskered jowls shook. "M-m-master, the Taira! Look! Their red b-banners!"

Yoshisune shot to his feet. "Red banners! Impossible! The Taira are no more. A year ago they died here at Dannoura!"

"But they come, Master, they come!"

Shizuka covered her face with her hands and sank to the bottom of the craft. For under a canopy of crimson flags twisting in the gale were advancing the ghosts of the slain Taira. Staring, hate-filled eyes glowed like firebrands through the dark. Wrathful faces quivered into shape and then dissolved like reflections in rippled water, only to reappear seconds later with gaping holes where chin or brow should be. Bloodless lips writhed.

An icy current raced through Yoshisune's veins. He feared neither man nor Tengu, but of what use was his sword against phantoms! In hordes they came, until the boat was surrounded by the ghostly warriors and their shrieks swelled above the clamor of wind and wave. Then two long arms spiraled out like the tentacles of an octopus to enclose Yoshisune and draw him from the vessel. He plunged his sword into the vaporous figure before him, but it was not there. The arms faded momentarily into a purple mist and then reached for him again. And now he felt himself being drawn to the side of the boat....

Benkei was on his knees, fumbling with his prayer beads. Then the voice that had boomed through the monastery of Mount Hiei chanting the long Buddhist prayers rose above the wailing of phantoms and howling of winds as he implored the gods to come to the rescue.

"Save us, Sacred Hachiman! Remember the Taira—how they reviled your temples and oppressed your priests! It was we, the Minamoto, who broke their evil power and sent them to the watery depths! Now, O Hachiman, keep them there!"

Twitching hands hovered over Benkei's head, and fingers stark as the iron ribs of a war fan began to close hungrily. Now the giant priest's voice swelled to a frenzied roar. "O Kwannon of the Thousand Hands! Goddess of Mercy! Deliver us from the

230

clutches of the rebellious dead!" Like volleys of thunder the impassioned prayers rumbled through the din-filled night.

Then the air was split with new sounds—cries of relief and joy from Yoshisune and the retainers. "They are retreating! We are saved! See, the Taira are sinking back into the water, and the red banners are no more! Benkei, mighty Benkei, again you have saved us!"

"Ya-a-a," said the giant with a wobbly grin, for his teeth still chattered, "I do all the dirty work!"

231

The ability to chant long sections of the Buddhist scriptures was one of the prime requisites of a priest. Such prayers, sutras, not only helped the souls of the dead to enter Paradise but also had the power to drive away evil spirits.

Legend says that sometimes during violent storms, fishermen in the region of Dannoura still see the grasping arms and hear the infuriated cries of the Taira ghosts.

The encounter of Yoshisune and Benkei with the phantoms has been dramatized in one of the No plays.

There are also ghostly fireflies. On the twentieth day of April thousands of people flock to the shores of the Uji River to watch the Minamoto and the Taira fireflies, ghosts of the old warriors, fight again the clan battles of the Twelfth Century. Millions of glowing insects flash from the shore to form a jeweled cloud over the dark river. On that night all caged fireflies are set free that they may join in the conflict.

yamaBushi

When the little band brought their boats to shore, they discovered that the ground was covered with the first snow of the season, and before them stretched wild, mountainous country. But there must be no delay: Benkei knew that they must press on before Yoritomo's spies began to trail them. A worried frown furrowed his face as he saw the footprints his party were leaving in the snow.

"We needn't make it so easy for the villains to find us," he grumbled. Removing his sandals, he replaced them backwards on his feet. The others followed his example, and then the trail in the snow looked like that left by a group of fishermen winding down to the sea.

Ever since their flight from Kyoto, Yoshisune's mind had been churning with possible plans for escape. Only one offered a glimmer of hope. "We must go back to Hidehira's stronghold in the North Country, Benkei. You remember the old ruler's last words: 'If ever you need help, come; here I will always give you my protection.' "

"Yes, Master, that is our best chance," replied Benkei. Yet, as they plodded on toward the hills, his frown deepened. As a wandering priest he had tramped all through these mountains, and he knew that they were filled with monks, many of whom would be delighted to curry favor with Yoritomo by capturing his fugitive brother. The young master's plan was good, but it needed a few additions.

Soon after nightfall Benkei crept away from his sleeping companions. He returned in the early dawn, arms and shoulders loaded with luggage boxes and with the clothes customarily worn by traveling priests.

Yoshisune was a bit startled. "More dirty work, Benkei?" he asked.

"Ya-a," laughed the giant. "Disguised as yamabushi, traveling priests begging alms for the gods, perhaps we can get through safely."

"Yamabushi! But Benkei, I know nothing of such things. What if I am asked questions?"

"Leave all the questions to me," answered Benkei. "Besides, Master," he added humbly, averting his eyes for a moment, "you will be safer in these." He handed his young lord the grass skirt, short jacket, and straw hat of a coolie—a servant!

Dressing and arming themselves—for yamabushi were expected to carry weapons as protection against brigands—they toiled up into the mountains. At the head was Benkei; at the rear plodded a heavily laden little coolie, straw hat pulled halfway down over his face.

For weeks they trudged toward the North Country, forcing their way through heavy woods, splashing across streams, struggling up steep paths. Always the travel was brutally hard, for Benkei led them through the most primitive trails, avoiding the main roads and villages where there would be curious eyes.

Then one morning as they curved their way around the brow of a hill, they found the path blocked by a large wooden barrier. On its top were the spiked heads of three yamabushi! There was

no time to turn or to hide. A guard had already seen them and was watching intently. Fear clutched at every throat like a savage beast. Benkei drew one long, deep breath and then stamped up to the barrier.

"What is the meaning of this," he bellowed, towering over the guard and pointing to the three spiked heads. "Why have you done this to my fellow yamabushi?"

"Orders, sir!" squeaked the guard, trying to shrink into his clothes like a turtle into its shell. "We have instructions to arrest Yoshisune and his party, who it is rumored are disguised as yamabushi. These heads belonged to three such reckless priests who tried to force their way past us."

"Are those Yoshisune and his men?" asked Benkei with seeming innocence.

"Of course not! If they were, would we be stopping you?"

"And this is how you treat those who collect alms for the gods! Out of our way!" growled Benkei.

"No," said the guard, still scared but resolved to hold his ground. "Only those with official orders are to cross the barrier."

"Orders!" roared the giant. "Well, why didn't you say so?"

Whipping a scroll from his sleeve, Benkei began to read in a sonorous voice: "I, Yoritomo, command all guards to let this group of yamabushi through. At my request they are collecting alms to restore the temple at Nara, which was destroyed by the Taira." On and on went the rumbling voice, giving explicit details as to size, location, and building plans. Long before Benkei had finished and swept the scroll back into his sleeve, the guard —overwhelmed with the torrent of words loosed upon him—had been bobbing his head up and down and fumbling at the locks of the barrier.

With silent prayers of gratitude for a Benkei who could read blank scrolls with such fluency, the travelers filed through the gate—right into a group of monks!

Not a muscle of Benkei's face twitched. Into their midst he went, with many bows and ejaculations of happiness at this un-

235

expected pleasure. Yoshisune, hovering behind him, heard him raise his voice in protest for a moment at the rude treatment they had received at the gate and then ask, "No doubt you will aid us with a rich contribution for the temple at Nara?"

The leader eyed him suspiciously and then said with a half-smile, "Yes. And you no doubt will answer some questions as to the Wheel of the Law that never goes backwards?"

Benkei beamed and bowed low. "At your service!"

"What are the four heavens?"

"They are on a mountain of four quarters. One side is of gold, another of silver, a third of lapis-lazuli, and the last of crystal."

"What is the meaning of the yamabushi headgear you wear?"

"Its circular shape symbolizes the universe and its twelve folds the twelve causes and effects."

"And the tassels on your scarf?"

"They refer to the four heavenly kings."

"What is the purpose of the yamabushi?"

"We roam mountain and valley, killing savage animals and serpents. In fair weather or foul we sleep in the mountains, and from this practice have acquired the name 'mountain sleepers.'"

"Why do yamabushi carry a conch shell?"

"To frighten evildoers and to summon other yamabushi if we become lost."

"And your black leggings?"

"To signify the darkness of the ocean. The eight-knotted sandals symbolize the petals of the sacred lotus flower."

"What is the most potent spell against demons?"

"Stand upright, beat your teeth thirty-six times, draw four horizontal and five vertical lines with your thumb."

On and on went the questions, Benkei answering them all without faltering. Well worth his time had been those days of study at Mount Hiei and his constant rambling through the hills. The examination ended. The leader was satisfied, the priests looked respectful, and the guards—awed at this display of learning—managed to close their gaping mouths.

"And now, Worshipful Master," said Benkei briskly, "those alms for the temple?"

Yoshisune swallowed a gasp. What a Benkei—collecting alms from the very priests who had been bent a short while before on collecting their heads!

"Fetch five rolls of silk and a quill of gold dust," ordered the head priest to a young monk. Not to be outdone, other priests and guards hurried off and brought back individual gifts for the good of their souls. Now it was Benkei's turn to gasp. This was a bit too much for the shoulders of his weary companions.

But he bowed low in gratitude and said, "May all the gods bless you. We are on our way to Noto but shall be back this way in a month. Allow us to leave some of the gifts until our return."

"As you wish," replied the priest.

Benkei had motioned the others to go on as he stayed behind to collect the alms. Now as he caught up with them, he saw that Yoshisune had been detained by a guard.

"What is this?" demanded the giant. "Why do you hold my worthless coolie?"

"Because he looks like Yoshisune, whom I saw several times in Kyoto."

"What!" cried the leader, who had followed Benkei to the gate. But before he had time to come forward for a close look, Benkei leaped forward, grabbed Yoshisune by the neck, and shook him as the wind shakes a scarecrow.

"Insolent wretch!" he bellowed. "How dare you look like a noble! By all the gods I'll teach you your place! Good-for-nothing laggard! You stagger under the slightest burden!" With that he began to beat Yoshisune so unmercifully with his staff that the prince crumpled to the ground. The other fugitives looked on in horror: Benkei beating his beloved master! On and on went the drubbing until even the priests and the guards were aghast and cried out.

"Stop!" said the leader. "This silly gatekeeper was mistaken. Take your coolie and be on your way!"

Still blustering indignantly for the benefit of the onlookers, Benkei dragged the limp Yoshisune behind him through the enclosure and out of sight down the narrow trail.

When the rest of the party caught up with them, they found Benkei on his knees before the prince. The huge shoulders were shaking with sobs. "Pardon, Master, pardon! Nothing is left for me but death! Allow me to conduct you safely to Hidehira's court and then cut me into a thousand pieces! Let me die in disgrace for having struck my lord!"

A quiet hand reached out to Benkei's heaving shoulders. The giant looked up to see a smile on the bruised face of his master.

"Noble, wise Benkei! You did what was necessary to save us. To lay down life for one's lord is expected and usual. To lay hands on him is to sacrifice one's deepest feelings. A story, Benkei. In the old days there lived a great man whose mother, in the time of his youth, had often been forced to punish him. At the age of thirty he again gave her occasion to do so. Surprised and annoyed at his loud wailing, she said, 'Even as a child you did not cry so much. Is it to make fun of me that you weep?'

" 'No, Blessed Mother,' he replied, 'I sorrow because the years have made your hand weak. I grieve for your waning strength.' "

"Angry with you, my Benkei? No, only proud—and grateful that our privations these many weeks have left you strong as you were." And the young prince of the Minamoto bowed his head low over the great hands of the warrior-priest.

238

The story of Benkei at the barrier, like so many of the stories in this book, is the theme of a No drama that is still played and loved in Japan.

Benkei's putting his sandals on backwards reminds one of the precocious little Greek god Hermes who—at the age of one day—stole Apollo's sacred cattle, forcing them to walk backwards so that the hoofprints would trail off in the wrong direction.

tortoise mountain

Weeks spun into months as the fugitives struggled on toward the North Country. Weariness dogged their footsteps; despair scourged their hearts. Sometimes it seemed as if malicious demons were tripping alongside, strewing the path with jagged rocks or gouging out treacherous holes to trap blistered, swollen feet. For despite their ever-increasing exhaustion, the travelers continued to take only the roughest and most tortuous trails in their attempt to avoid Yoritomo's men, who now seemed to be everywhere. Again and again the travelers were stopped and questioned; but the nimble-tongued Benkei, whose wits had become as sharp as his sword, squeezed through every snare. Meanwhile, his bag of alms for the temple at Nara continued to swell.

Sometimes the snares appeared to be too open, and then the giant suspected that there were those who still remembered—and loved—the dauntless prince who had broken the power of the Taira.

The day came when the young wife, who had borne the hardships of the journey uncomplainingly, could go no farther. Yoshisune and Benkei spread cloaks for her under a gaunt pine tree and there in the mountain stillness a baby was born. The mother called for water, and Benkei stumbled through brambles, around cliffs, and into ravines to find a mountain brook, but there was none. In anguish of spirit he struck a barren rock with his two hands, and a hidden spring gushed forth. Gratefully he filled his conch shell.

When he came back with the precious liquid, Yoshisune was holding the child in his arms. "So little I can give you, my son. Like a wild, hunted thing you are born, for like a wild, hunted thing is your father."

"Not so, my lord," said Benkei, and the voice of the giant who could fight a hundred men at once was as gentle as that of the young mother at whose side he had dropped to bathe her forehead. "This too shall pass; again you shall be a prince and a commander of men."

Pale and silent on her crude bed, but with eyes soft as the wings of a dove, the mother whispered: "For many weeks, my lord, Death has skulked behind us, but we defy him by bringing forth new life. Be comforted, and rejoice in your son."

Benkei's hands reached for the child. "Let me name him," he said. "Son of Yoshisune, you shall be called Prince Tortoise Crane because we are on Tortoise Mountain and because the crane lives many years. May you be wise and gallant as Yoshisune, strong as Benkei."

They dared not linger long. Striking out again for the narrow trail, they trudged on through the mountains. And it was in the arms of Benkei that the wee Prince Tortoise Crane was cradled.

Then one morning they saw the straw-thatched roofs of a village in the valley below. "The outskirts of Hidehira's stronghold!" breathed Yoshisune. No more barriers, spies, guards. Were they to find peace and safety at last?

When Yoshisune came to Hidehira's palace, the wise and kind old ruler received him in full ceremonial costume that he might show his respect and honor. Grasping the hands of the weary prince in welcome he said, "I am glad that you have come, son of my friend. Rest here in peace."

With bowed head Yoshisune told him of the brilliant triumphs over the Taira on land and sea, of the brother's growing jealousy, and of the ignominious flight from Kyoto. Hidehira listened, and his heart swelled with compassion for the gallant youth who had tasted both the sweets of supreme triumph and the gall of hopeless defeat.

Yoshisune fell silent. The old ruler took his hand and murmured, "The tall, antlered deer is the first to be seen by the hunter, and the towering pine is whipped by every storm." After a while he continued: "Several miles down the river is a new palace. It is yours. As long as I live you will be safe there, for I will give you my protection."

"As long as I live..." That night Hidehira tossed restlessly on his bed, still stung by the brooding despair in Yoshisune's eyes. Yes, Hidehira was honored to give sanctuary to the staunch young prince. "But I am old; ninety summers have I seen. My jealous sons who will rule after me when I am gone, what will *they* do?"

The palace provided for Yoshisune was located on a series of three hills that afforded easy defense on sides and rear. Guarding the front was a swift-flowing river. High walls surrounded the courtyard. Thus the fugitives felt safe for the first time in many months. The face of the young mother again became like the petals of a flower as she played with Prince Tortoise Crane. Yoshisune read in the ancient Chinese books and pondered how the wisdom of the past could help him guide his own uncertain footsteps into the future. For Hidehira sent word that Yoritomo had discovered Yoshisune's place of refuge and now was demanding his head.

Hidehira's reply was swift and incisive: "I choose to protect the Prince of the Minamoto!"

Yoritomo—unable to challenge successfully the powerful old military chieftain—fretted, watched, and waited.

a thousand to one

It was in the springtime, when peach blossoms were bowing gracefully to every breeze, that a messenger came from Hidehira. "My lord is ill," he said, "and wishes to see you at once."

Yoshisune flung himself on his horse and sped down the tree-lined highroad, his thoughts pounding as thunderously as the steed's hoofs. His good friend! Must he lose him too?

The old ruler's breath was already coming in gasps when Yoshisune arrived. "My son," he quavered, "for many months I have tried to soften your brother's heart toward you, but now I know it is useless. Leave this land! Go to the island of Yezo in the north, where the barbaric Ainu dwell. From there cross the Western Sea to the vast country beyond. A great destiny is yours—but not in the land of your ancestors as you had hoped. See, here are maps of Yezo's roads and waterways; for many years my scouts have worked on them."

Yoshisune caught his breath sharply. "Strange that you should urge me to go to Yezo. Now I would tell you a tale. Only this morning my faithful retainer Kaison returned from hunting in the hills. He had wandered too far in search of the elusive deer and had become lost. A light flickering through the dusk caught his attention, and he followed its gleam. It led him to a small shelter of boughs, with only a bed of leaves inside and a small campfire without. Before this simple dwelling an aged hermit knelt in prayer. He welcomed my henchman and invited him to share the evening meal of stewed fruits. 'Stay with me tonight,

Kaison, and tomorrow I will show you the road back through the mountain.'

"My henchman was astonished. 'How did you know my name?' he asked.

" 'Ah,' said the old man, 'many years I spent learning Senjutsu, the art of a mystic. Now I am more than three hundred years old; I know all things, and the future unfolds before me like a scroll.'

" 'Then tell me what is to become of my master, Yoshisune, son of Yoshidomo,' said Kaison.

"The old sage hesitated; then, with a deep sigh, he took the shoulder blade of a deer and held it over the flame until it was scorched and seared. Carefully he examined the cracks. 'Yoshisune is safe for the moment, but danger looms ahead. He must not tarry longer. Let him go to the lands beyond the Western Sea. There, the lot says, he can become king and lord of vast domains. The chance is his; let him not cast it away.' Then the aged hermit threw the bone far from him and would say no more."

Hidehira clasped the shoulder of the young prince. "Then go, Yoshisune, and may Kwannon of the Thousand Hands guide and bless you!" The old ruler died, murmuring the name of his cherished friend Yoshidomo, whose son he had protected.

Now Yoshisune and Benkei worked swiftly, studying the maps and gathering provisions for the flight into Yezo. But already Yoritomo's warriors, long hovering in readiness, were on the march. For Hidehira's greedy sons, eager to win favor with the powerful Shogun, had sent word of their father's death.

"Lands and riches for the head of Yoshisune!" had come the reply.

Plans were almost completed that morning when the call to attack sounded. Benkei and Yoshisune hastened to the wall. Advancing toward them was an army of sixteen thousand men.

"And we are but sixteen strong!" said Benkei grimly. "The knaves do us much honor in measuring our strength at a thousand to one!"

Yoshisune grasped his hand. "If this is the end, good friend and comrade, at least we shall put a great price on our lives."

Two of the henchmen ascended the roof of the main building to keep watch on the enemy from all sides, while the others raced out to guard the entrance. Old Hidehira had planned well for the defense of the palace. The one road that led to the gate was constructed along the crest of a steep narrow bank that fell so sharply away on both sides that an armed warrior could not find a foothold. At this point the small band faced an army.

Wave after wave of Yoritomo's men swarmed onto the road, to find it blocked with warriors who fought like demons. The assailants fell in heaps before the ferocious defense until at length, scarcely able to believe their eyes, the captains called for a temporary retreat.

Benkei and nine of his men staggered back behind the walls, but four of the valiant fighters lay motionless outside the gate.

Again came the attack; again the defense that swept warriors down like cornstalks in the path of a raging fire. All day long

Yoritomo's troops struggled in vain to storm the palace gates. At dusk the baffled captains called for another retreat, but now only two defenders—Benkei and Saburo—were left to creep back inside the walls. The giant did not stay there long. Though bleeding from a dozen wounds, he emerged from the enclosure alone and threw himself once more upon the enemy. A thousand to one! Benkei made good that boast.

But now he knew that the end was near. Leaving Saburo to watch the gate, he went into the palace to see his beloved master once more. He found Yoshisune, dressed in white, reading a prayer from the Buddhist scriptures. The voice was clear and unshaken. Beside him sat his lady, head bowed over little Prince Tortoise Crane.

Benkei paused at the door. For once in his life he could not speak. Yoshisune's quiet eyes met his. The giant priest dropped to his knees and faltered, "Master, the end has come. Our men are gone; only Saburo and I remain. I have come to be with my lord for one last moment."

The kneeling man felt tender hands on his shoulders. "My Benkei! In victory and in death—always my devoted, faithful Benkei! Do not mourn. Evasion and flight have been our lot. Now they are at an end."

"Where you go, Master, I go," whispered Benkei.

A cry shattered the stillness and the giant rose, his great heart breaking, to help his companion at the gate. He stumbled from his master's presence into the courtyard just in time to see Saburo beaten to the ground.

Now the strength of all those heroic, fallen comrades seemed to flood through every vein of Benkei's lacerated body. Never had the twelve-foot glaive swung with such might; never had the giant evoked such abject terror. In panic the assailants fled, to take a position beyond the river.

On a narrow shoal in the center of the stream, Benkei made his stand. Legs stretched wide apart, back braced against a boulder, he formed a barricade that no man could pass. All night the Yoritomo warriors, propelled relentlessly forward by their commanders, surged into the water; all night long Benkei's glaive swirled, slashed, and cut.

With the rising of the moon, the captains called their bowmen. Thousands of arrows whistled through the night to the black armored figure in the middle of the stream, but still he stood—erect, immobile. Brave warriors talked in awed whispers: was this a man, a demon, or a god?

Then dawn lightened the eastern skies. Incredulous murmurs rose as the giant figure in the river became clearly visible. Like quills of a porcupine, arrows bristled from every crevice of his black armor. But he stood!

A few brave bowmen went into the water to discharge their arrows at closer range. Nearer they came, until they saw the rigid face, still an angry red from the reflected glow of the red lacquer that lined Benkei's helmet. Braced against a rock, the Black Priest of the Western Pagoda was dead—on his feet and unconquered to the end.

Now the troops burst into the palace, from which flame and smoke were already billowing. In a small room, gray with smoke, they found the body of a young warrior dressed in rich brocade and splendid armor. At his feet were white, blood-stained mats, mute testimony that he had committed the ancient ceremony of harakiri, the taking of one's own life. A few minutes would have cheated the besiegers from finding him at all, for the book he had been reading was already half consumed with fire.

"Is it Prince Yoshisune?" asked a captain.

"Yes," answered one of his men. "I know this armor well."

Severing the head, they put it in a jar of wine to preserve it. Forty-three days later it was placed before Yoritomo in his citadel at Kamakura.

"The head of Yoshisune as you ordered, my lord," said the captain. Gloating, the Shogun peered into the tub and then turned to the old counselor by his side: "Now, Kajiwara, we can rest comfortably."

and yet–

There are those who say that Yoshisune did not die that night. No, they say, it was not his body in the smoke-drenched room but that of a faithful retainer who had donned Yoshisune's robes and armor that his master might escape without fear of pursuit. And the head? How could Yoritomo identify with certainty a head that had been jostled along rough roads in a tub of wine for forty-three days?

There are also those who maintain that Benkei too escaped during the blackness of night after fastening his helmet and armor to a straw-stuffed dummy to draw the arrows of the enemy.

Had not Hidehira given Yoshisune a map of the roads and waterways of the northern island of Yezo? And do not the Ainu, inhabitants of Yezo, to this very day speak Yoshisune's name reverently and worship him in a shrine built to his memory? "He became king and ruled wisely," say the Ainu, "but after a time he went over to the great continent."

"Go to the country beyond the Western Sea," Hidehira had urged. "A great destiny is yours, but not in the land of your ancestors...."

Toward the end of the Twelfth Century, in Tartary—the country just beyond the upper tip of Yezo, labelled Hokkaido on your maps—a brilliant young chieftain who called himself "Temujin" began a series of conquests that brought one nomadic tribe after another under his control. Never had the fierce Mongols had a leader so fast with the sword or so brilliant in strategy.

Men flocked to his white banners; young boys, who had learned to ride as babies by clinging to the woolly backs of sheep, yearned for the day when they could join Temujin's band of horsemen.

Over northern and central Asia, down into Russia, Poland, Hungary, and onto the threshold of Austria swept the ever-growing hordes of Mongolian conquerors until it seemed as if the whole world would come under their sway. The mysterious Temujin had accomplished the seemingly impossible: he had united all the wild tribesmen of the steppes into one gigantic clan.

Then he began to call himself Genghis Khan, and the name struck terror to millions. His countless horsemen carried no supplies, living entirely off the land. Many a thriving village and city was left denuded and desolate as the conquering hordes swept over them like human locusts. Yet it seems that Genghis Khan never destroyed deliberately: when the land sufficed to feed both his tribesmen and the inhabitants, he established a just and efficient rule. Churches never were harmed, and priests of all faiths were respected. Rigid laws quelled disorder and brought a higher level of peace and civilization than many people had ever known before.

Post roads were established in the wilderness; couriers, with bodies greased to help them endure the winter cold, carried the chieftain's commands to all parts of the empire. Two hundred miles a day the riders covered, bells jingling from saddles to warn other travelers out of the way. Fresh ponies waited at well-spaced encampments.

But the power-loving Khan relished luxury and beauty also. When his hordes overran Cathay, he lived in magnificent palaces of jade and crystal. Rare flowers graced his gardens, and the stepping stones that curved among fountains and trees were lotus leaves carved from precious gems. Here too the Khan's law was so well obeyed that carts of gold and silver could stand in the open, unguarded.

Temujin—a fitting pseudonym for a prince who had learned swordsmanship from the King of the Tengu; Genghis—so much like Genji, which was another name for the Minamoto clan; Gen Gi Kei—Chinese characters that are used to express both Yoshisune and Genghis Khan; white banners streaming over Mongolian encampments as they had over Dannoura; Khan meaning "running water," and Minamoto meaning "water source."

But whether he died in northern Japan as a fugitive from his brother's injustice or as the mighty conqueror who ranged from end to end of the Orient, Yoshisune lives in the minds of the Japanese as one of their most noble and gifted heroes. Unswerving loyalty to a cause, military skill, selflessness—these are qualities the Japanese revere. In Yoshisune they find them all.

It was in the Seventeenth Century that distinguished scholars first presented evidence linking Yoshisune with Genghis Khan. Then in 1867 a scroll was discovered that told of Yoshisune's escape from Japan to Yezo, a retainer having given his life that his head—which closely resembled Yoshisune's—might be sent to the vengeful brother. In 1879 a Cambridge University student wrote a book pointing out the mystery of Genghis Khan's origin and his sudden appearance on the Asiatic scene shortly after Yoshisune's reputed death. Were Yoshisune and Genghis Khan the same person? The question remains unanswered.

hoichi the earless

Many years had passed since the sea battle of Dannoura. In the temple that had been built to pacify the spirits of the defeated Taira lived a blind priest named Hoichi. From childhood he had been entranced by the tales of the fierce contest that had sent the Taira fleet to the bottom of the sea, and in time he became famous for his skill in chanting the stories to the accompaniment of his biwa.

One evening as he sat alone on the veranda, he heard someone approach. Then a deep, unfamiliar voice called "Hoichi!"

"Who are you?" asked the blind priest.

"My honorable lord and his followers have come to the village to see the scene of the battle of Dannoura. He has heard of your skill and wishes you to entertain his company with an account of the conflict. He asks that you come at once."

Hoichi, flattered at the stranger's request, bowed his head in agreement. Then he felt a firm hand on his shoulder and heard the clank of armor as the stranger led him through the temple grounds and down a long pathway. A sharp command, and a gate was opened. Hoichi heard the sound of many feet and the rustling of silk robes.

A soft-voiced woman led him up a flight of steps and bade him be seated. "All is ready," she told him. "Now let us hear of the battle at Dannoura."

A hush fell over the company, and Hoichi began to chant to the accompaniment of his biwa. Quietly at first and then with

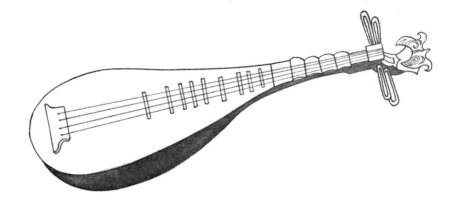

rising fervor, the blind priest told the story of intrigue, pursuit, terror, and despair. So skillful was he that the twang of arrows and swish of waves crept into his instrument, and a murmur of admiration arose from the listeners. But when he came to the account of the child-emperor Antoku plunging into the sea with his guardian, the appreciative murmurs turned to anguished lament, and he fell silent.

"My lord is delighted with your performance," said the man who came to lead him back to the temple. "He wishes you to return tomorrow. I will come for you. But tell no one of these visits."

The next night Hoichi played again before the distinguished company, and again he moved them first to applause and then to tears. Never before had the priest had so responsive an audience, and he resolved that the third night his biwa would ring out more eloquently than ever.

But the head priest had observed his absence and, fearing some harm to the blind man, had followed him into the night. To his amazement he saw Hoichi enter the cemetery, sit at the tomb of the child-emperor Antoku, and begin to chant the story of the battle of Dannoura. All around him eerie fires glowed fitfully, and low moans rose and fell with the cadences of the biwa.

"Hoichi! Hoichi!" shouted the priest. "You are under an evil spell! Stop at once!"

But Hoichi played on, a rapt smile on his face and the glow of the ghostly fires in his staring eyes. Louder and more vibrantly swelled his voice until it seemed that the sound was being wrung from his very soul. Then he subsided into a whisper. Still oblivious to the frenzied shouts of his friend, he bowed low, murmured thanks to his audience, and allowed himself to be led back to the temple as if in a dream. With food and drink before him, Hoichi threw off the strange spell and told the head priest all that had happened.

"You are in great danger, Hoichi. It is not the house of a great lord that you have been visiting, but the Taira cemetery. Your skill has caused the spirits to become restless again. By obeying them you have put yourself in their power, and they are certain to harm you."

"How can I escape?" asked the frightened musician.

"I must go away tonight," said the priest, "But before leaving I will see that your entire body is covered with sutras. These sacred writings will break the evil spell of the ghosts."

Hoichi was stripped. With a writing brush a monk inscribed sutras upon his head, face, chest, back, limbs—even the palms

of his hands and soles of his feet. Then the head priest gave final instructions. "You will be visited again tonight, but you must not answer. Sit still and make no sound, whatever happens."

That evening as the blind musician sat on the veranda, the sound of heavy footsteps came as before and a voice called "Hoichi!" So terrified that he could scarcely breathe, the priest sat like a stone. The footsteps came nearer and the voice, now tinged with anger, again called "Hoichi!"

"No answer? I'll find the fellow!" Then the horror-stricken priest heard the stranger walk toward him across the veranda. "What!" came the voice. "Here is the biwa, but where is the player? I see only two ears! No mouth: that is why he could not answer. But I will take these ears to my lord."

Hoichi felt clammy hands close about his ears and rip them from his head. But despite the pain, not a sound escaped him. Then he heard the stranger stalk away.

When the head priest returned and saw Hoichi, still sitting motionless on the veranda, he wept with dismay. It's all my fault, no, it's all that careless monk's fault! I told him to write sacred texts everywhere on your body. He missed your ears. They alone were unprotected from the restless Taira ghosts! Be comforted, though, for you will never be bothered with the phantoms again."

But poor Hoichi soon discovered that in addition to losing his ears he had lost his taste—his taste for stories about the Taira and their defeat by the Minamoto at Dannoura.

A Buddhist temple is the residence of Buddhist priests. Invariably there is an attached cemetery, and it is the chief duty of the priests to chant prayers for the souls of the dead. Each temple has a Buddhist image to whom the prayers are addressed.

As seen in the story of Hoichi, the chanting or writing of Buddhist scriptures, the sutra, are potent spells.

The biwa makes the sound of "bi" when a string is pushed in and that of "wa" when pulled out—hence its name. The four strings of the instrument symbolize the four seasons of the year.

the kusanagi sword

254 "I *must* get the Kusanagi Sword; only then can I subdue the barbarian rebels who dare to challenge my authority!"

The chief minister bowed low before the Emperor Go Shira-kawa. "Long have I searched the ancient records, Your Majesty. No one has seen the sword since it sank into the waters of Dannoura with the child-emperor Antoku and his guardian so many years ago."

"Through divination we shall learn how it can be regained," said the emperor. "Let ceremonies be performed in all the temples."

His orders were carried out. Then one night a court lady dressed in the morning robes of a long-ago day appeared to him in a dream. Through softly undulating waves she came, and her eyes were deep and sad. "The Kusanagi Sword lies in the Palace of the Dragon King below the waters at Dannoura," she said. "If you would thrust back the barbarians, recover it, O Emperor!"

Go Shirakawa summoned the two best divers in Japan, a mother and her daughter. "Descend to the bottom of the sea and bring back the divine sword," he commanded.

They were taken in a boat to the deep waters where Antoku had been drowned. The priests performed a ceremony, and the women dived into the waves. Many hours passed before they reappeared.

"Wondrous things we have seen!" they said. "In the depths of the ocean we came to a city with walls of coral and gates of pearl.

But we were not permitted to enter, for a holy man stepped in our path. 'Without the help of Buddha you can come no farther,' he told us."

Then said the emperor, "Let charms be placed about the women that they may try again."

They were taken· to the temple, and there the chief priest wrote sutras on strips of cloth, which the divers wound about their bodies. A second time they plunged into the sea; a second time they returned without the sword.

"Ah, but we saw it! Catching sight of our sutras, the sentinels at the gates bowed low and permitted us to enter the city of gleaming towers. Through silver-paved streets and along avenues where trees bore jewels instead of fruit we passed until we came to the Palace of the Sea God. 'At the command of our emperor we have come for the Kusanagi Sword,' we told the guards. They looked at us strangely, and then a maiden came forward to lead us to the great hall of the palace. There we saw a huge serpent with a magnificent sword in its mouth and a boy asleep in its coils.

"The serpent spoke: 'You cannot have the sword, for it belongs to me. Many ages ago when Japan was very new the weapon was taken from the sea kingdom by a dragon prince in the form of a serpent. A deity slew him, took the sword, and gave it to the Sun Goddess. She in turn presented it to her grandson Ninigi when he came to earth. His descendants, the Japanese emperors, kept it for many centuries until a sea dragon transformed itself into a mortal princess. In time that princess became the guardian of the child-emperor Antoku. When she leaped into the sea at Dannoura with the boy, the sword was girded to her belt. Now both Antoku and the sword are mine.'"

Emperor Go Shirakawa was not to be turned from his purpose. He must get the sacred weapon! "Let there be more charms, more sutras," he decreed. "This time the women will be successful."

Once again the divers went down to the Palace of the Sea God, still more heavily laden with the powers of Buddha. And now the serpent could no longer resist. Reluctantly he gave up the sword, though the child continued to doze contentedly in his coils. Then the women returned to the surface of the waves in triumph, holding the sword aloft.

Through its divine power the barbarians were driven from the land, and the grateful emperor placed the holy object in the Atsuta Temple.

But the fame of the Kusanagi Sword reached far beyond the sea. Foreign rulers, longing to possess the treasure for themselves, sent spies to search the land for it. One day a Korean youth came to the temple as a priest. No one suspected him, but his keen eyes watched and his ears listened. Finally his chance came. He seized the sword and concealed it in the folds of his robe. But at that moment a cloud descended upon him, and from it came an arm that grasped the sacred weapon and returned it to its resting place.

For many days the youth performed magic ceremonies and chanted sutras; again he took the sword. This time, protected by the powerful charms, he was able to steal away from the temple. But that night as he lay asleep, the cloud entered his room and took the sword as before.

Then the determined young priest evoked even stronger charms and once more stole the sacred treasure. Now success seemed to be his, for he reached the coast and set sail for Korea. But his triumph was short-lived: a mighty tempest churned over the waves, and the boat began to flounder.

"The Sea God is showing his wrath!" cried the captain. "Which one among you has offended him?"

The youth knew at last that never could he take the sacred sword from Japan. He threw it into the seething waters; there a divine messenger waited, ready to carry it back to the temple.

And there to this day lies the Kusanagi Sword, one of the Three Sacred Treasures of the Land of the Eight Great Islands born so long ago to Izanagi and Izanami—the celestial pair who stood on the Floating Bridge of Heaven and churned the waters below to form an earth.